中国国家汉办规划教材

体验汉语系列教材

体验汉语®

Experiencing Chinese

生活篇
Living in China

顾　问　刘　珣

总策划　刘　援

编　者　宋海燕　詹成峰

练习册
Workbook

高等教育出版社
Higher Education Press

《体验汉语®》立体化系列教材

短期课程系列：

《体验汉语®生活篇练习册》（附mp3）

顾　　问　　刘　珣
总 策 划　　刘　援
编　　者　　宋海燕　　詹成峰

策　　划　　徐群森
责任编辑　　王　丽
版式设计　　刘　艳
插图选配　　王　丽
插图绘画　　刘　艳
封面设计　　周　末
责任校对　　王　丽
责任印制　　宋克学

前言

本书是为配合《体验汉语·生活篇》的使用而编写的一本练习册，针对每单元的学习目标和学习内容，提供了丰富多样的活动和练习，用于补充课堂教学和课后复习。

基本结构

本书和《体验汉语·生活篇》一致，共有12个单元。每单元分为课堂活动和课后练习，其中课堂活动又分两部分。

一、课堂活动

课堂活动与主教材保持一致，每单元分两部分，每部分前一个或两个活动可供导入教学参考使用，其他主要是为巩固相应语言功能项目、实现学习目标而编排的。

二、课后练习

该部分设置若干练习题，全面复习每单元涉及的语音、词汇、语法和汉字，训练听、说、读、写等技能。

主要特色

突出语言和实际生活的相关性。学习语言的最终目的是交际，因此，本书充分考虑到语言内容与学习者实际生活的相关性，在基础性训练的基础上，力求做到活动和练习真实、实用，如学习数字时尽可能地呈现实际生活中的真实材料，包括门牌号、公交站牌、车牌号、电话号码等，做到学有所用、学则能用。

注重复习和学习相结合。本书在注重复练的同时，也着意适当补充新内容，引导学习者在练习中学习吸收。这主要体现在两个方面：一是生词。本书根据实际需要增加了一些教材中没有但生活中常用的词，为其加注拼音和翻译，如“早饭”、“上班”等。二是阅读仿写或仿做。每单元阅读部分都为学生呈现与教材内容相关但教材中没有体现的项目，让学生模仿学习，如名片、便条、请假条等。

强调趣味性和互动性。本书力争从激发学习者兴趣的角度出发，安排了实景图片、小组活动、采访、游戏等，并在每单元的最后一项练习中设置让学习者亲身实践的任务，以引起学习者的兴趣，实现学练目标。

使用建议

课堂活动应结合课堂教学进行，学生一般要在老师的指导下完成。

课后练习附参考答案，学生可作为家庭作业，也可作为自测题目，检验学习效果。如果需要，教师也可以有选择地作为课堂练习使用。

本书第1、3、6、9、10、12单元由宋海燕编写，第2、4、5、7、8、11单元由詹成峰编写。

美国专家王宇老师在练习编写的“相关性”和“趣味性”方面给予了很大的启发，在此深表谢意，同时也感谢高教社编辑的辛苦工作。当然，囿于水平，书中难免会有缺点和错误，也真诚希望您对本书提出宝贵意见和建议。

编　者

2006年6月

目 录 CONTENTS

Unit 1 你好！

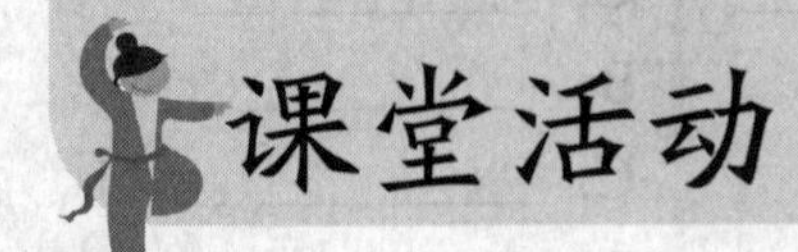

课堂活动

第 1 部分

一、听老师用汉语介绍自己的名字

Listen to the teacher introducing himself/ herself in Chinese.

二、模仿例句，告诉老师你的名字

Tell the teacher your name as given in the example.

例： 你好！我姓宋，叫宋丽丽。

三、看图说出下列人物的名字

Look at the pictures and tell the names of the people.

张子玉
Zhāng Zǐyù

李英杰
Lǐ Yīngjié

欧阳 明
Ōuyáng Míng

四、两人一组，完成对话

Work in pairs and complete the following dialogues.

A. 张文 Zhāng Wén

B. 李慧娟 Lǐ Huìjuān

C. 马良伟 Mǎ Liángwěi

例：A —— B	A —— C	B —— C
A: 你好！您贵姓？	A: 你好！您贵姓？	B: ________
B: 我姓李，叫李慧娟。	C: 我姓____，叫______。	C: ________
A: 李小姐，你好！	A: ______，你好！	B: ________
B: 你好！您贵姓？	C: 你好！您贵姓？	C: ________
A: 我姓张，叫张文。	A: 我姓____，叫______。	B: ________
B: 张先生，你好！	C: ______，你好！	C: ________

五、两人一组，根据实际情况完成对话

Work in pairs and complete the following dialogue with your true information.

A: 你好！

B: ________

A: 您贵姓？

B: 我姓________，叫________。您贵姓？

A: 我姓________，叫________。

六、仿照例句采访班里3个同学，完成表格

Follow the example and interview three of your classmates to complete the form.

例： 你好！您贵姓？你叫……？

	姓	名
1		
2		
3		

七、学练数字

Practise using numbers.

1. 看图读数字。Look at the following picture and read the numbers.

48, 67, 53, 77, 92, 108,

277, 388, 396, 444, 666

2. 小游戏：明7暗7。Game

全班同学围成一圈，一个同学用汉语说任一数字（最好100以内），他左边的同学说出该数字的下一个数字，如第一个同学说3，下一个同学说4，依次类推。

凡遇到7的倍数（如7, 14, 21, 28……）和含有7的数字（如17 ,27 ,37……）的同学要拍手通过，不能说出该数字来，如果说出来，该同学就输了，大家可以要求他表演一个节目。

The whole class gathers around in a circle. One of the classmates says any number (within 100) in Chinese. The classmate on his left then says the next number. For instance, the first student says 3 and the next says 4. The game goes on like this. Those who come across the multiples of 7 (like7,14,21,28...) and the numbers comprising 7 (like 17,27,37...) should clap their hands instead of saying the numbers out loud. If the number is said aloud, the one loses and will have to conduct a special performance as a penalty.

3. 用汉语回答下列问题。Answer the following in Chinese.

(1) 一支足球队在场上有多少人?

(2) 一支篮球队在场上有多少人?

(3) 班里今天有多少人来上课?

(4) 你一天有几节课?

(5) 你一周有几节汉语课?

(6) 一年有多少天?

4. 问问你班里同学的电话号码并记下来，做成通讯录。
Ask your classmates for tionstheir telephone numbers, then write them down to make an address list.

	姓名	电话号码
1		
2		
3		
4		
	……	

第2部分

一、听老师自我介绍
Listen to the teacher introducing himself/ herself in Chinese.

二、模仿例句，向老师介绍自己
Introduce yourself to the teacher as given in the example.

例： 你好！我姓宋，叫宋丽丽。我是中国人。

三、角色扮演
Role-Play

请同学表演第一课第二部分的会话，可以加上必要的表情和动作。

Please perform the dialogue in the second part of Lesson One, adding facial expressions and gestures when necessary.

四、两人一组，看图完成对话
Work in pairs and complete the following dialogues according to the pictures below.

1. A：你是中国人吗？
   B：__________
2. A：你是哪国人？
   B：__________

3. A：你是法国人吗？
   B：__________
4. A：你是哪国人？
   B：__________

① 

② 

③ 

④ 

五、两人一组，完成对话
Work in pairs and complete the following dialogue.

A：你好！

B：＿＿＿＿＿＿

A：您贵姓？

B：我姓＿＿＿＿，叫＿＿＿＿＿。您贵姓？

A：我姓＿＿＿＿，叫＿＿＿＿＿。

B：你是哪国人？

A：我是＿＿＿＿人。你呢？

B：我（也）是＿＿＿＿人。

六、按要求填写卡片，然后交给老师

Fill in the card as requested and hand it to the teacher.

姓：＿＿＿＿＿＿

名：＿＿＿＿＿＿

国　籍(nationality)：＿＿＿＿＿＿

课后练习

一、听录音，填写声母或韵母

Listen to the recording and fill in the initial or the final sound of a syllable.

_ín

_ěn

_én

g__
g__
n__
n__

二、听录音，标出声调
Listen to the recording and mark the tones.

jiao wo ye guo shi ying

三、听录音，选出你听到的音节
Listen to the recording and check(✓) the syllables you have heard.

sì	( )	shì	( )
hǎo	( )	hěn	( )
běn	( )	hěn	( )
guó	( )	guì	( )
nǐ	( )	nín	( )

四、听录音，选出你听到的句子
Listen to the recording and select the sentences you have heard.

1. 你好！　　您好！
2. 你贵姓？　　您贵姓？
3. 我是英国人。　　我不是英国人。
4. 您是美国人吗？　　您是哪国人？

五、听录音，选择合适的应答语组成会话
Listen to the recording and select the suitable replies to make up dialogues.

1. ( )　　A. 不是。
2. ( )　　B. 我也是中国人。
3. ( )　　C. 你好！
4. ( )　　D. 我姓张。
5. ( )　　E. 我是英国人。

六、看汉字，写拼音

Look at the Chinese characters and write down the *pinyin* (the Chinese Phonetic Alphabet) for them.

您 好 很 人 是 哪

七、选词填空

Fill in each of the blanks with the proper word.

姓 是 很
1. 我 ________ 宋。
2. 我 ________ 中国人。
3. 我 ________ 好。

哪 呢 吗 也 不
4. 他是 ________ 国人？
5. 你好 ________？
6. 我是中国人，你 ________？
7. 你姓张，我 ________ 姓张。
8. 马丁是美国人，________ 是英国人。

八、用括号里的词改写句子

Rewrite the sentences using the words in given the brackets.

他是中国人。

1. ______________________________ （也）
2. ______________________________ （吗）
3. ______________________________ （不）

九、将下列句子排成一段有意义的对话

Rearrange the following sentences to form a meaningful dialogue.

我是中国人。你呢？　　我是美国人。您贵姓？

你是哪国人？　　我姓张，叫张华。

A: ______________________________

B: ______________________________

A: ______________________________

B: ______________________________

十、回答下列问题
Answer the following questions.

1. 您贵姓？

____

2. 你是中国人吗？

____

3. 你是哪国人？

____

4. 我叫马丁，你呢？

____

十一、填空
Fill in the blanks.

你好！我姓________，叫________，我是________人。

十二、看图并回答问题
Read and answer the questions.

1.

(1) 这个人姓什么？

____

(2) 这个人叫什么？

____

(3) 他的邮编(postcode)是多少？

____

(4) 他的传真号码(fax number)是多少？

____

2. 个人小档案

姓 名：刘 勇（Liū Yǒng）
性 别：男
国 籍：中 国
生 日：1983.7.13
身 高：188cm
体 重：74kg

（1）他姓什么？

____

（2）他叫什么？

____

（3）他是哪国人？

____

（4）他的身高是多少？

____

（5）他的体重是多少？

____

十三、数一数下列汉字的笔画，按由少到多的顺序排列

Count the strokes of the Chinese characters and arrange them in the order of ascending numbers of stroke.

我　　也　　姓　　叫　　是　　好

____　____　____　____　____　____

十四、写出有下列部首的汉字

Write down the Chinese characters that consist of the following parts.

1. 亻：____ ____
2. 女：____ ____
3. 口：____ ____ ____ ____

十五、按笔顺将下列汉字书写五遍

Write the following Chinese characters five times each, following the appropriate stroke order.

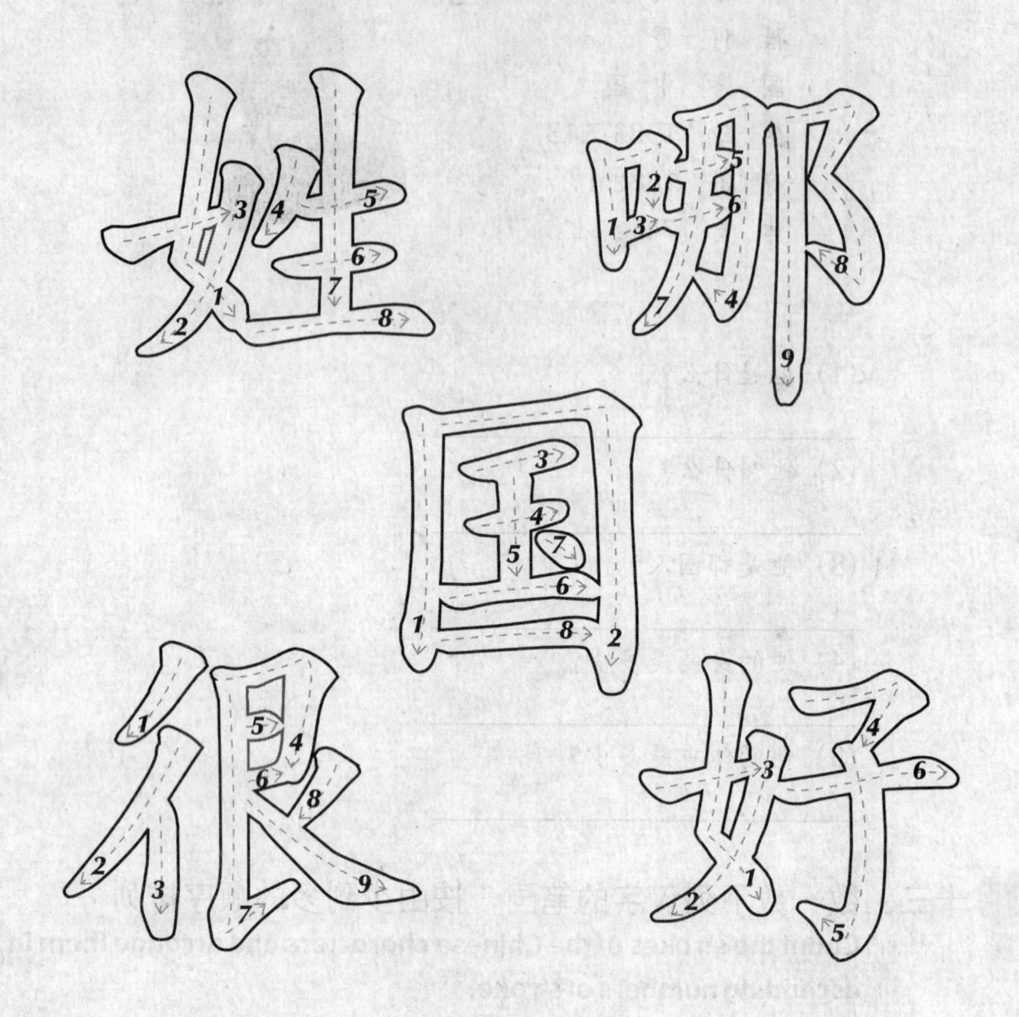

十六、实践活动：为自己制作一张中文名片

Practice: Create a Chinese name card for yourself.

Unit 2 现在几点？

课堂活动

第1部分

一、复习数字，学习时间表达法

Review the numbers and learn how to tell the time.

1. 用汉语说出老师写在黑板上的数字(100以内)。Use Chinese to say the numbers (within 100) that the teacher wrote on the blackboard in a loud voice.

2. 按下列要求数一数。Count out the number as requested.

   (1) 班里有多少男生？多少女生？

   (2) 班里多少人戴眼镜？多少人不戴眼镜？

   (3) 班里多少人是长头发？多少人是短头发？

   (4) 班里多少人穿牛仔裤？多少人穿运动鞋？

小词表

戴 dài wear

眼镜 yǎnjìng glasses

牛仔裤 niúzǎi kù jeans

运动鞋 yùndòng xié sports shoes

3. 请用汉语说出你昨晚睡觉和今早起床的时间。Use Chinese to tell the time you went to bed last night and the time you got up this morning.

4. 跟老师用汉语说出下列图示的时间。Tell the teacher the time indicated in the following pictures in Chinese.

九点

九点零五（分）

十点十五（分）/十点一刻

十一点半/十一点三十（分）

十二点四十五（分）

八点五十五分/差五分九点

5. 掌握下列表示时间的词。Please learn the following words that indicate the time.

点、分、刻、半、差、零、过

二、用汉语说出图中的时间

Use Chinese to tell the time as shown in the picture.

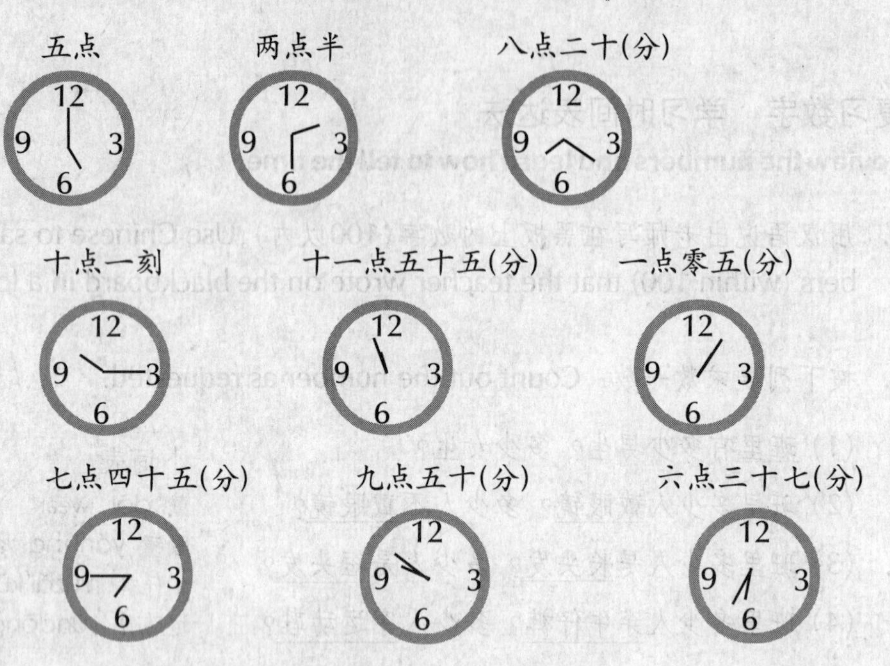

三、两人一组，用汉语说出表中时间，完成句子

Work in pairs, then follow the example to tell the time in the schedule and complete the sentences.

起 床 6：30 qǐ chuáng get up	例：王先生 六点半 起床。
早 饭 7：05 zǎo fàn have breakfast	王先生 ________ 吃早饭。
上 班 8：30 shàng bān go to work	王先生 ________ 上班。
午 饭 12：00 wǔ fàn have lunch	王先生 ________ 吃午饭。
下 班 5：30 xià bān get off work	王先生 ________ 下班。
晚 饭 6：45 wǎn fàn have dinner	王先生 ________ 吃晚饭。
睡 觉 22：15 shuì jiào sleep	王先生 ________ 睡觉。

四、两人一组，仿照例句讨论一天的作息安排，完成表格

Work in pairs, then follow the example to discuss the daily schedule and complete the form.

例： 甲：你几点起床？

乙：我六点起床。你呢？

甲：我六点半起床。

	我	同学
起　床		
吃早饭		
上　学		
吃午饭		
放　学		
吃晚饭		
做作业		
看电视		
睡　觉		

五、看图回答问题

Look at the pictures and answer the questions.

1. 营业时间 Business hours

邮局几点开门？

几点关门？

银行几点开门？

几点关门？

2. 办公时间 Office hours

他们上午几点上班？

下午几点下班？

办公时间

上午 8:30－12:00

下午13:00－17:00

六、根据下面的场景练习对话
Practise the dialogue according to the following situations.

（1）早上，在学校门口　（2）下午，在公司门口　（3）中午，在写字楼的餐厅

甲：现在几点？

乙：现在 ________。

甲：你几点 ______？

乙：我 ___ 点 ______。你呢？

甲：__________。

第2部分

一、表达日期
Telling the date

1. 请用汉语说出对你来说最重要的一个日子。Use Chinese to indicate the most important day in your life.

2. 请用汉语说出一周中你最喜欢哪一天。Use Chinese to indicate your favorite day of the week.

二、根据实际情况和老师一起回答问题
Answer the questions according to your practical situation.

答

1. 今天几号？　　今天 ___ 月 ___ 号。

2. 今天星期几？　　今天星期 ___。

3. ___ 号是星期几？　　___ 号是星期 ___。

三、两人一组，完成对话

Work in pairs and complete the dialogue.

甲：今天几号？

乙：今天___月____号。

甲：今天星期几？

乙：今天星期____。

甲：____号是星期几？

乙：____号是星期____。

四、两人一组，互相提问，完成下表

Work in pairs and then complete the following forms by asking each other questions.

表1

问　题	日　期	
	我	同　学
1. 你的生日		
2. 你爸爸的生日		
3. 你妈妈的生日		
4. 你中学毕业的日子		
5. ……		

表2

问　题	星　期	
	我	同　学
1. 一周中你最不喜欢的是		
2. 你有汉语课的是		
3. 你们俱乐部有活动的是		
4. 你作业最多的是		
5. ……		

五、在纸上写下3个你最近要去或想去的地方，然后两人一组谈谈计划

Write down three places that you will visit or would like to visit in the near future and work in pairs to talk about your plans.

例： 甲：你几号去香港？

乙：我12号去香港，23号回北京。

六、抽签问答，请抽到问题的同学按顺序提问，抽到相应答案的同学回答

Please draw lots. Those who get the questions should ask them in turn; those who get the answers should give the corresponding replies.

今天几号？	二十号是星期天。
你几号去上海？	我二十号回北京。
你几号回北京？	我下午六点回家。
二十号是星期几？	现在八点半。
现在几点？	我晚上十一点睡觉。
你几点回家？	今天九月七号。
你几点睡觉？	我十五号去上海。

七、两人一组，选择下面的问题进行会话，至少用上三个问题

Work in pairs, then choose at least three from the following questions to make a dialogue.

现在几点？
今天星期几？
今天几号？
你几点__________？
你几号__________？
你星期几__________？
你呢？
______号是星期几？
星期______是几号？

例： 甲：现在几点？

乙：现在十一点二十分。

甲：你几点吃午饭？

乙：我十二点半吃午饭。你呢？

甲：我十一点半吃午饭。

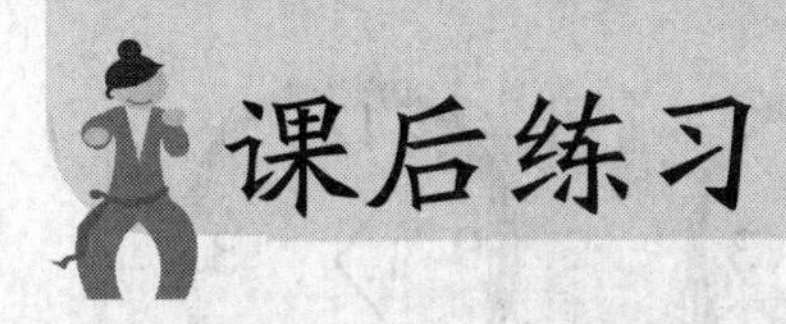

课后练习

一、听录音，填写声母或韵母
Listen to the recording and fill in the initial or the final sound of a syllable.

__iàn
__iān
__iǎn
__àn

h__
h__
h__

二、听录音，标出声调
Listen to the recording and mark the tones.

qu　yue　qi　ji　hui

三、听录音，选出你听到的音节
Listen to the recording and select the syllables you have heard.

1. jǐ　(　)　nǐ　(　)
2. hǎo　(　)　jiǎo　(　)
3. yīng　(　)　xīng　(　)
4. qù　(　)　qī　(　)
5. rì　(　)　shì　(　)
6. jiā　(　)　jīn　(　)

四、听录音，按听到的顺序在相应的图下面写上序号
Listen to the recording and write down the sequence number below the corre-

sponding pictures according to the order of what you have heard.

1.

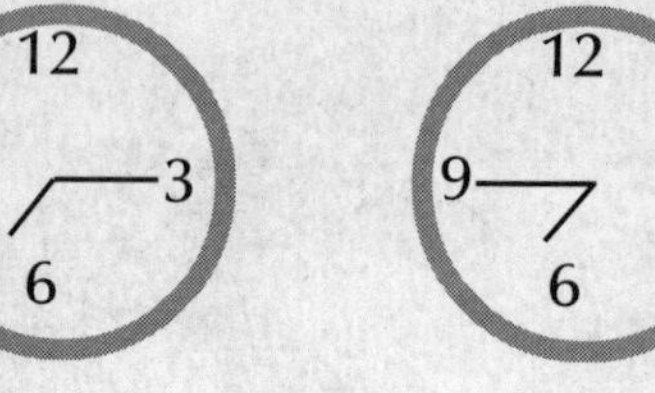

(　　)　(　　)　(　　)　(　　)

2.

星期一 13号	星期六 18号	星期四 16号	星期日 19号
(　　)	(　　)	(　　)	(　　)

五、听录音，选择正确答案

Listen to the recording and choose the correct answers.

1. A. 一点。　　B. 七点。
2. A. 十二号。　　B. 二十号。
3. A. 星期四。　　B. 星期五。

六、看汉字，写拼音

Look at the Chinese characters and write down the *pinyin* (the Chinese Phonetic Alphabet) for them.

去　　　现在　　　今天　　　星期

七、看拼音，用汉字写出句子

Look at the *pinyin* and write down the sentences using Chinese characters.

1. Nǐ jǐ diǎn huí jiā?
2. Xīngqīliù shì jǐ hào?

八、根据提示填上相应的时间词
Fill in the corresponding words that indicate the time as prompted.

1.

星期二 6号	星期三 7号	星期四 8号	星期五 9号	星期六 10号
______	______	今天	______	______

2.

6:00	9:00	12:00	16:00	20:00
早上	______	中午	______	______

九、按正确的顺序把下面的词语排列成句
Arrange the following words into properly ordered sentences.

1. 点　几　上班　你

____?

2. 我　三　星期　去　北京

____。

3. 星期　五　九　二十　号　今天　月

____。

十、回答下列问题
Answer the following questions.

1. 昨天星期几?

____

2. 昨天几号?

____

3. 现在几点?

____

十一、完成下面的短文
Complete the following short passage.

今天______月______号，星期______。我早上______点起床，______点去上学。中午______点吃午饭。下午______点回家，______点吃晚饭。晚上______点睡觉。

十二、看图并回答问题
Read and answer the questions.

1. 北京大学的上课时间表 The class timetable of Peking University

第一节	8:00—8:50
第二节	9:00—9:50
第三节	10:10—11:00
第四节	11:10—12:00
第五节	12:30—13:20
第六节	13:30—14:20
第七节	14:40—15:30
第八节	15:40—16:30
第九节	16:50—17:40
第十节	17:50—18:40
第十一节	19:10—20:00
第十二节	20:10—21:00

（1）上午几点开始上课？晚上最后一节课到几点？

______________________________。

（2）每天多少节课？

______________________________。

（3）上午第三节几点上课？下午第三节几点下课？

______________________________。

2. 王先生本周的日程表　　Mr. Wang's schedule this week

	星期日	星期一	星期二	星期三	星期四	星期五	星期六
日期	18	19	20	21	22	23	24
上午		去上海	见客户			开　会	
下午				回北京			
晚上							朋友聚会

(1) 王先生几号去上海？几号回北京？

____

(2) 星期几见客户？

____

(3) 星期四是几号？

____

(4) 几号开会？

____

(5) 什么时候朋友聚会？

____

3. 北京大学2006学年第二学期校历　The school calendar of the 2006 academic year of Peking University

第二学期（2006.2.16—2006.6.25）

		一	二	三	四	五	六	日
0	2006年				16	17	18	19
1	二　月	20/27	21/28	22	23	24	25	26
2				1	2	3	4	5
3		6	7	8	9	10	11	12
4	三　月	13	14	15	16	17	18	19
5		20	21	22	23	24	25	26
6		27	28	29	30	31		
7		3	4	5	6	7	1/8	2/9
8	四　月	10	11	12	13	14	15	16
9		17	18	19	20	21	22	23
10		24	25	26	27	28	29	30
11		1	2	3	4	5	6	7
12		8	9	10	11	12	13	14
13	五　月	15	16	17	18	19	20	21
14		22	23	24	25	26	27	28
15		29	30	31				
					1	2	3	4
16		5	6	7	8	9	10	11
17	六　月	12	13	14	15	16	17	18
18		19	20	21	22	23	24	25
		26	27	28	29	30		
	七　月	3	4	5	6	7	1\8	2\9

一、	学生选课：2月16日－17日 学生注册：2月20日－24日 2月20日全校开始上课
二、	全校运动会： 4月21－23日（21日停课）
三、	"五一"放假 5月1日－5日放假，4月29、30日，5月6、7日照常休假。
四、	非毕业班学生（本科生）停课 复习考试：6月12日－23日 6月26日开始放暑假
五、	毕业教育及毕业资格审查：6月26日－30日 毕业典礼：7月3日－4日 办理离校手续：7月5日－6日

1. Course selection: February 16 — 17
   Registration: February 20 — 24
   School begins on February 20.
2. Athletic meeting: April 21 — 23 (Classes will be suspended on April 21)
3. May Day holiday: May 1 — 5 being the vacation, while April 29, 30 and May 6, 7 are the normal days off.
4. Classes suspended for non-graduating students (undergraduate students)
   Exam review: June 12 — 23
   The summer vacation begins on June 26.
5. Graduate education and graduation certificate examination: June 26 — 30
   Graduation ceremony: July 3 — 4
   School departure procedures: July 5 — 6

1. 这个学期一共有多少个星期？ ______________________
2. 哪一天开始上课，哪一天开始放假？ ______________________
3. 运动会是什么时候？ ______________________
4. "五一"放假几天？ ______________________
5. 毕业典礼是什么时候？ ______________________

十三、数一数下列汉字的笔画，把笔画数写在下面
Count the strokes of the following Chinese characters and write the numbers of stroke below.

几　　点　　回　　家　　月　　号

_____ _____ _____ _____ _____ _____

十四、找出下列每组汉字中相同的部件
Find the common components within each of the following groups of Chinese characters.

例： 后　回　号　（口）

1. 昨　明　晚　（　）
2. 明　期　朋　（　）
3. 星　是　早　（　）

十五、按笔顺将下列汉字书写五遍
Write the following Chinese characters five times each, following the correct stroke order.

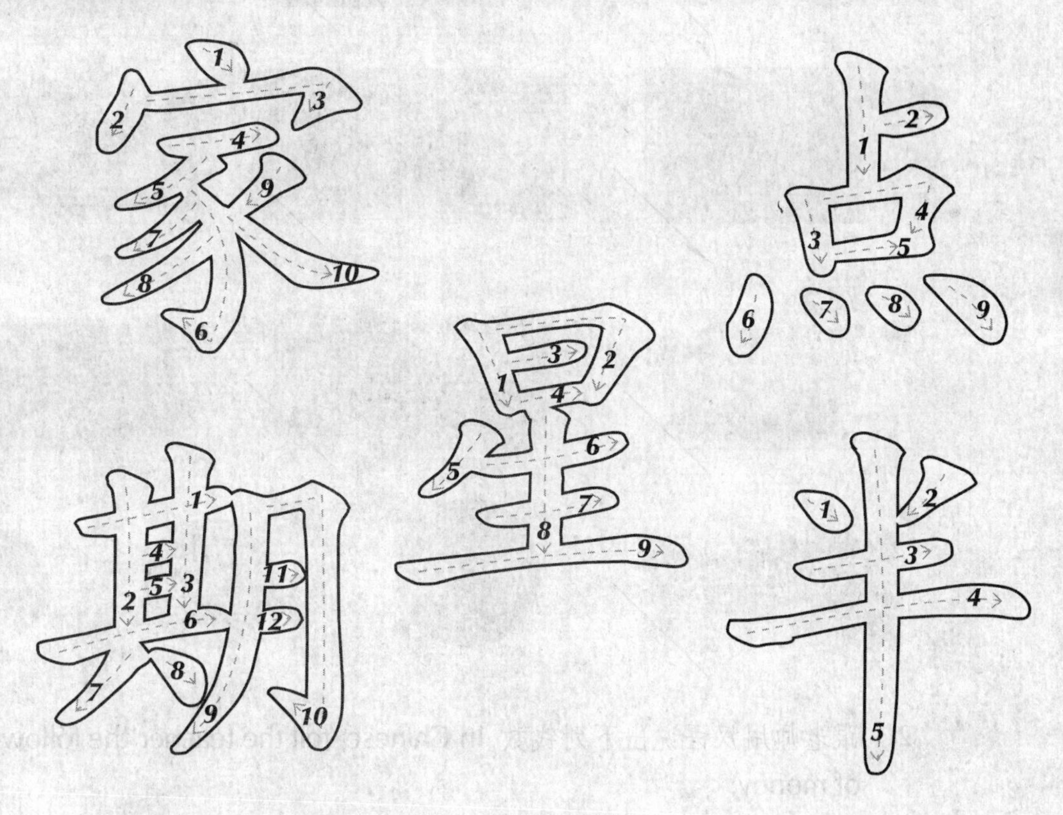

十六、实践活动：用汉语制作一个本校的校历
Practice: Create a school calendar of our university in Chinese.

Unit 3 那件毛衣怎么卖？

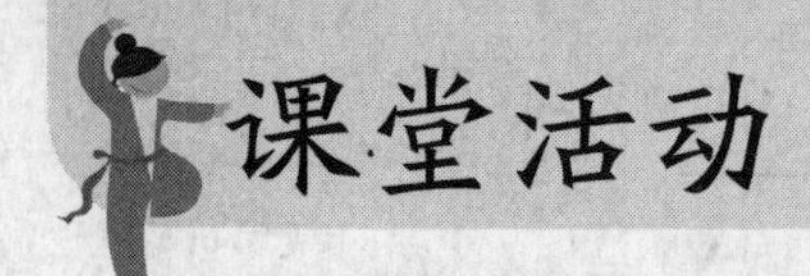

第1部分

一、学练人民币的表达

Learn the expressions about the chinese currency Renminbi.

1. 看图认识人民币。Recognize the chinese currency Renminbi through each picture.

2. 跟老师用汉语说出下列钱数。In Chinese, tell the teacher the following amount of money.

二、看图说出钱数

Look at the pictures and tell the amount of money.

例： 一百三十元

1\.   ________

2\.   ________

3\.     ________

三、两人一组，互相提问，完成下表

Work in pairs and ask each other questions to complete the following form.

问 题	价 钱	
……多少钱？	我	同学
1 你的汉语课本		
2 你买过的最贵的东西		
3 你一个月的电话费		
4 ……		

四、两人一组，看图完成对话

Work in pairs, then look at the pictures and complete the dialogues.

A：你好！你买什么？
B：我买________。多少钱一斤？
A：________一斤。
B：太贵了，便宜点儿，行吗？
A：________。要多少？
B：要________斤。一共多少钱？
A：________________。

西红柿：3.50

荔枝：15.00

五、买卖游戏

Game: Buying and Selling.

全班同学分成A、B两组，A组为卖者，写出或画出自己最爱吃的水果和价钱。B组为买者，每人买3种水果，完成表格。两组可以轮流进行。

The whole class is divided into Group A and Group B.The students in Group A are sellers,who should write the words or draw the fruit they like best with its price.The students in Group B are buyers,and each of them can buy three kinds of fruit and put them in the following form.The two groups can play in turn.

A组

B组

	水果	单价	数量（斤）	总价
例	苹果	2.50	2	5.00
1.				
2.				
3.				

参考句子：

你买什么？	我买……。
……一斤。	……多少钱一斤？
要多少？	太贵了，便宜点儿，行吗？
	……要……斤。
	一共多少钱？

第2部分

一、按要求回答

Answer the questions as requested.

1. 用汉语说出你今天所穿的衣服。Name the clothes you are wearing today in Chinese.

2. 用汉语说出在教室里能看到的颜色。Identify the colors that can be seen in the classroom in Chinese.

二、看看班里哪个同学有你感兴趣的东西，去询问价钱并完成下表

See which classmate has something that interests you, ask its price, and complete the following form.

问：你的……多少钱？

	东西	价钱（元）
例	马丁 的 毛衣	98.00
1.	________ 的 ________	
2.	________ 的 ________	
3.	________ 的 ________	
4.	……	

三、角色扮演

Role-Play

请同学模仿表演第三单元第二部分的会话，可以加上必要的表情和动作。

Please imitate and perform the dialogues in the second part of Unit 3, adding expressions and actions when necessary.

四、每人抽一张词语卡片。按反义词、名词和量词的要求分成每两人一组

Each student should take a vocabulary card. The class should be divided into groups of two, based on the classification of antonyms, nouns and measure words.

大	肥	长	薄	便宜	小	厚
这	短	买	瘦	贵	卖	那
夹克	裤子	皮鞋	条	件	双	

五、按上题的分组，看图完成对话

Look at the pictures and complete the dialogues according to the above grouping.

皮鞋：￥166

夹克：￥130

裤子：￥89

1. A：那双皮鞋怎么卖？
   B：________。
   A：有____的吗？
   B：对不起，没有。

2. A：那____ ______怎么卖？
   B：________。
   A：有____的吗？
   B：有。
   A：我试试，行吗？
   B：行。
   A：这____ ______太____了，
   有____的吗？
   B：对不起，没有。

3. A：那____ ______怎么卖？
   B：________。
   A：有____的吗？
   B：有。
   A：我试试，行吗？
   B：行。
   A：这____ ______太____了，有____的吗？
   B：你试试这件。
   A：这件很好。太贵了，便宜点儿，行吗？
   B：行，______（价钱）。/对不起，不行。

六、抽签问答。请抽到问题的同学提问，抽到相应答案的同学回答

Draw lots. Those who get the questions should make the indicated enquiries and those who take the corresponding answers should reply accordingly.

你买什么？	我要两斤。
草莓怎么卖？	我买面包。
你要多少？	十块一斤。

一共多少钱？	对不起，没有黑的。
那套西服怎么卖？	行。
有黑的吗？	你试试这件，这件薄一点儿。
我试试，行吗？	一共二十块五。
这件夹克太厚了，有薄的吗？	三百六一套。

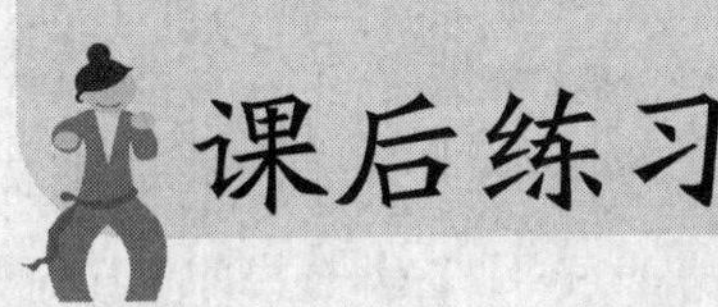

课后练习

一、听录音，填写声母或韵母

Listen to the recording and fill in the initial or the final sound of a syllable.

__ āi
__ ài
__ iǎo
__ áo

m__
m__
g__
g__

二、听录音，标出声调

Listen to the recording and mark the tones.

pian duo liang zhe shen you yao hong yi xing

三、听录音，选出你听到的音节

Listen to the recording and select the syllables you have heard.

xíng ( ) xìng ( )
mǎi ( ) mài ( )
nà ( ) dà ( )

tāi （　　）　　mài （　　）

cǎo （　　）　　xiǎo （　　）

四、听录音，选出你听到的词或句子
Listen to the recording and select the words or sentences you have heard.

1. 一点儿　　一点
2. 你要多少？　　你买多少？
3. 太大了，有小的吗？　　太小了，有大的吗？
4. 我要黄的。　　我要红的。

五、听录音填空
Listen to the recording and fill in the blanks.

1. 草莓要 ______ 斤。　　2. ______ 件夹克怎么卖？
3. 我买 ______。　　4. 有 ______ 的吗？

六、听录音，选择正确答案
Listen to the recording and choose the correct answers.

1. 他买什么？
   A. 草莓　B. 苹果

2. 他买几斤？
   A. 四斤　B. 十斤

3. 一共多少钱？
   A. 十四块　B. 三十块　C. 十二块　D. 三十五块

七、填量词
Fill in the measure words.

1. 一 ______ 毛衣
2. 一 ______ 裤子
3. 一 ______ 西服
4. 一 ______ 苹果
5. 一 ______ 皮鞋

八、反义词连线
Connect the antonyms.

大　　　　那
瘦　　　　卖
贵　　　　小
厚　　　　短
这　　　　胖
买　　　　薄
长　　　　便宜

九、连词成句
Make sentences by linking the words.

1. ______________________?
   钱　一共　多少
2. ______________________?
   卖双　这　怎么　皮鞋
3. ______________________?
   的　小　吗　有

十、用括号里的词语完成对话
Complete the dialogues using the words in the brackets.

1. A：______________?（裤子）
   B：一百八。
2. A：______________?（黑）
   B：有。
3. A：______________?（试）
   B：行。
4. A：______________?（太……了，长）
   B：你试试这件。
5. A：这件很好。______________?（太……了，便宜）
   B：行，一百五。

十一、看图并回答问题

Read and answer the questions.

1.

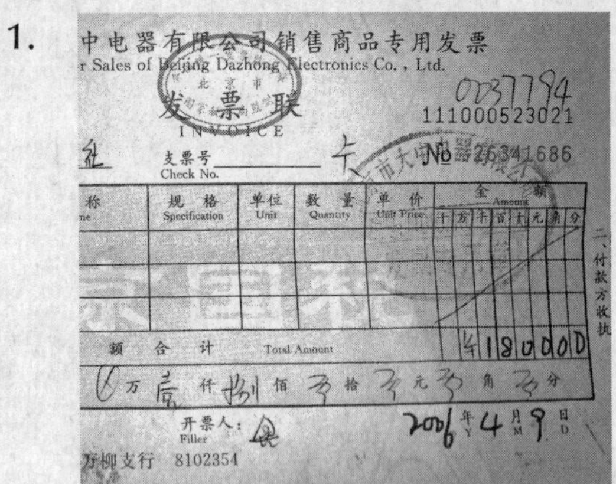

中电器有限公司销售商品专用发票
r Sales of Beijing Dazhong Electronics Co., Ltd.
发票联
INVOICE
111000523021
№ 26341686
支票号
Check No.

称	规格 Specification	单位 Unit	数量 Quantity	单价 Unit Price	金额 Amount
额 合计 Total Amount					¥180000

开票人：
Filler
万柳支行 8102354

(1) 发票上显示花了多少钱？

____

(2) 发票是什么时候开的？

____

2.

华中商场
亚运村店 电话：(010) 64910099

2006年 7月19日 17:37 <027>

苹果	10.70
草莓	29.00
商品数量	1点
合计	39.7
现金	100.00
零钱	60.30

No. 00270 赵燕

(1) 买了哪些东西？

____

(2) 一共花了多少钱？

____

(3) 什么时候买的东西？

____

十二、把笔画数相同的字写在一起

Put together the Chinese characters that have the same numbers of stroke.

买　什　么　多　少　钱　斤　两　块

十三、写出下列汉字的部首

Write down the parts that form the following Chinese characters.

汉字：苹　钱　块　行　件　试　红　这

部首：____ ____ ____ ____ ____ ____ ____ ____

十四、按笔顺将下列汉字书写五遍

Write the following Chinese characters five times each, following the proper stroke order.

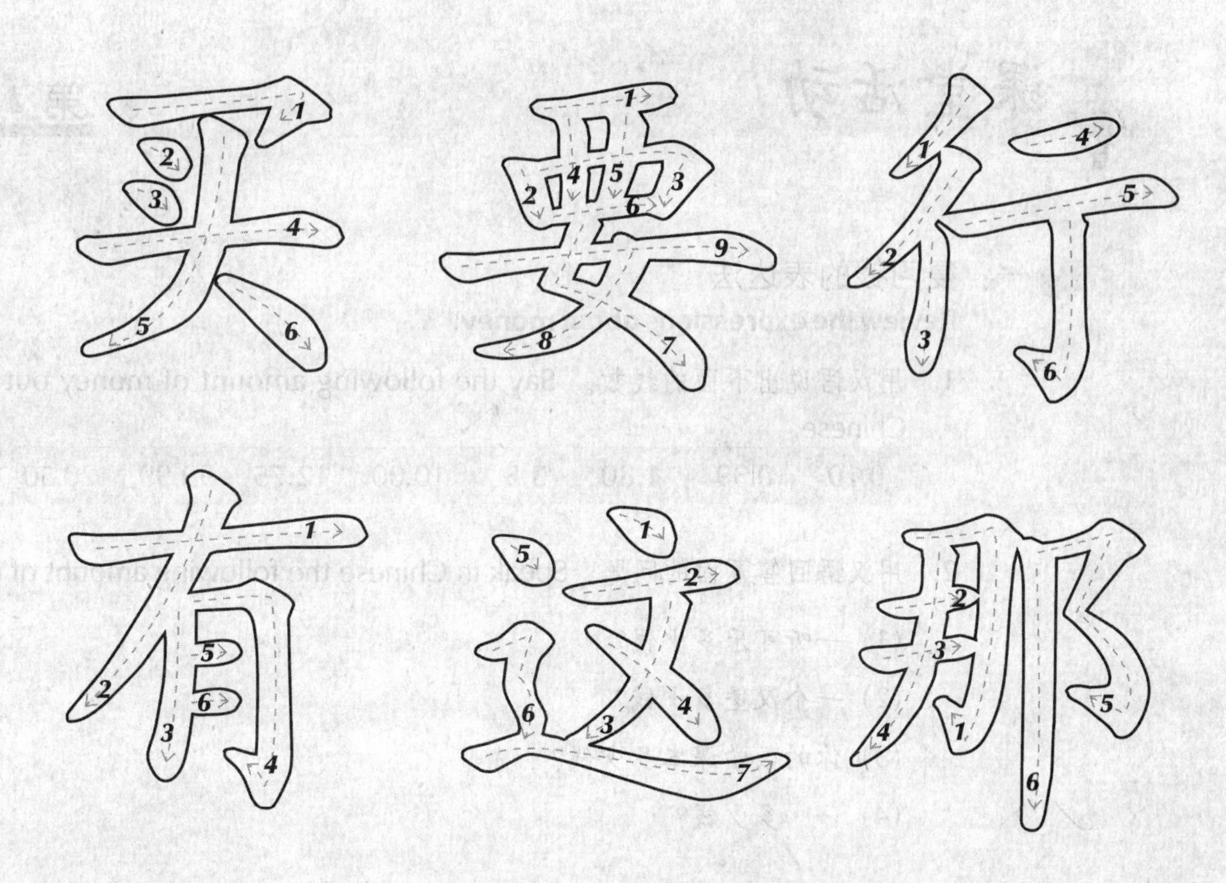

十五、实践活动：去中国人开的商店买东西，然后用汉语做一个账单

Practice: Go shopping at a Chinese shop and draw up a bill in Chinese.

日　期：			地　点：		
	商品名称	单　价	单　位	数　量	总　价
例	毛衣	120	件	1	120
1.					
2.					
3.					

Unit 4 要一个宫保鸡丁

课堂活动

第1部分

一、复习钱的表达法

Review the expressions about money.

1. 用汉语说出下面的钱数。Say the following amount of money out loud in Chinese.

0.10	0.39	1.80	3.5	10.00	12.75	99.99	120.50	1030.70

2. 用汉语回答下面的问题。Speak in Chinese the following amount of money

(1) 一听可乐多少钱?

(2) 一个汉堡多少钱?

(3) 你的数学课本多少钱?

(4) ……多少钱?

二、复习中国菜名

Review the names of Chinese dishes.

1. 用汉语说出你去过的中国餐厅的名字。Use Chinese to name the Chinese restaurants that you have been to.

2. 用汉语说出你吃过的中国菜的名字。Use Chinese to name the Chinese dishes that you have tasted.

三、请用汉语说出下列菜品饮料的名称

Use Chinese to name the following dishes.

四、请用汉语说出下列餐具的名称

Please speak in Chinese the names of the following tableware.

五、每人抽一个词，说出恰当的量词

Each student will draw a word and then pronounce the appropriate measure word.

例： 烤鸭——一只烤鸭

一（　）烤鸭	一（　）松鼠鳜鱼	一（　）鱼香肉丝	一（　）西兰花
一（　）饺子	一（　）面条	一（　）馒头	一（　）米饭
一（　）酸辣汤	一（　）可乐	一（　）橙汁	一（　）绿茶
一（　）筷子	一（　）盘子	一（　）勺子	一（　）汤碗
一（　）茶杯	一（　）餐巾纸	一（　）刀子	一（　）叉子

六、两人一组，扮演服务员和顾客，利用第三、四、五题中出现的词语完成对话

Work in pairs, then play the parts of waiter and customer respectively using the words you have learnt in Exercises 3,4, and 5 to complete the dialogue.

例： 服务员：这是菜单，请点菜。

顾　客：要一个宫保鸡丁，一个鸡蛋西红柿汤。

服务员：还要别的吗？

顾　客：再要一碗米饭。

服务员：您喝什么？

顾　客：要一壶绿茶。

七、假设你们在下面的情况下要在一家中国饭馆吃饭，菜单如图所示，请讨论并选择你们要点的菜（热菜、汤、主食、饮料）

In the following scenario, you will be eating at a Chinese restaurant. The menu is shown in the picture. Please discuss and choose what you would like to order(hot

dishes, soups, main courses and soft drinks).

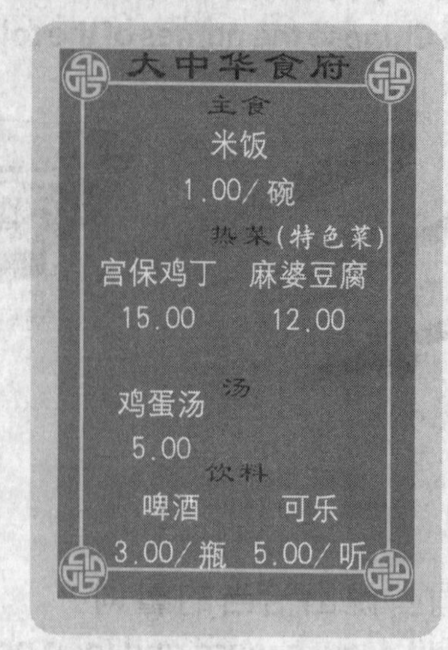

(1) 你和你的好朋友，两个人都喜欢吃辣的、酸甜的，你们准备花80元左右。

(2) 你和你的父母，三个人，准备花120元左右。

第2部分

一、请跟老师用汉语说出你的要求。

Make your request, then communicate it to the teacher in Chinese.

1. 你需要一张餐巾纸。
2. 你不喜欢菜里面放味精。
3. 你不吃辣的。
4. 你不吃香菜。
5. 你不喜欢吃蒜。
6. 你希望菜不要太咸。
7. 你很饿，希望你的菜能快点儿上来。
8. 你需要打包带走。
9. 你要结账。

二、根据图片练习句子

Practise the sentences as indicated by the pictures.

例：(1) 请给我<u>一张餐巾纸</u>。

(2) 别放<u>香菜</u>。

三、在下面的情况下，你说什么
What would you say in the following cases?

1. 你点完菜了，半个小时还没上。

   ____

2. 你没有时间在饭馆吃饭，想带回家吃。

   ____

3. 你吃完饭，准备付钱。

   ____

四、假如你去中国饭馆吃饭，点完菜以后，你还有哪些特别的要求对服务员说？在老师的帮助下弄清楚相应的汉语说法
If dining at a Chinese restaurant, what special requests do you need to make of the waiter after ordering? Make the equivalent Chinese expressions clear with the help of your teacher.

1. ______________________________
2. ______________________________
3. ______________________________

五、每人抽一句话，找出和你的句子意思相同的同学组成一个小组
Each student draws a sentence. The class should be divided into groups, with individuals whose sentences have the same meaning grouping together.

这是菜单，请点菜。	要什么酒水、饮料？
要一个宫保鸡丁。	服务员，餐巾纸。
您喝什么？	服务员，我们的菜快点儿。
请给我一张餐巾纸。	好的，请稍等。
这个菜打包。	来一个宫保鸡丁
能快点儿吗？	这是您要的餐巾纸。
小姐，结账。	这是菜单，您来点儿什么？
好的，马上。	服务员，买单。
好。给您餐巾纸。	打包。
……	……

六、按第五题的分组扮演顾客和服务员，练习对话（可以利用第二题、第三题的词语）
Play the parts of waiter and customer respectively according to the grouping of

Exercise No.5 and practise the dialogue. (You may use the words in Exercises No.2 and No.3)

例：

（马丁点完菜了）

马丁：服务员，别放味精。

服务员：好。

马丁：请给我一张餐巾纸。

服务员：好。给您。

马丁：谢谢。

（二十分钟后）

马丁：服务员，我们的宫保鸡丁还没上，能快点儿吗？

服务员：我去看看。

（吃完饭了）

马丁：服务员，结账。

服务员：一共七十八块。

马丁：这两个菜打包。

服务员：好。

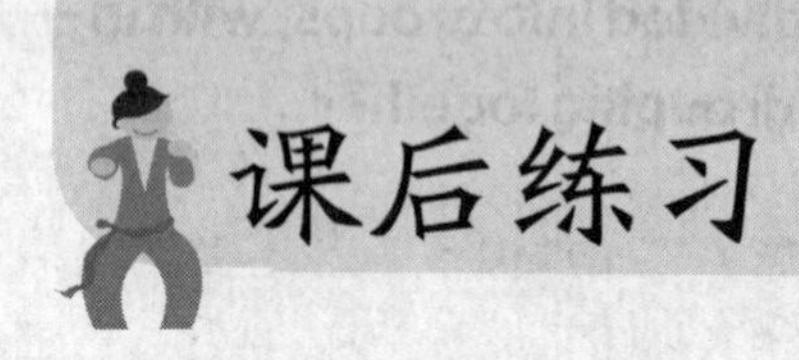

课后练习

一、听录音，填写声母或韵母

Listen to the recording and fill in the initial or the final of a syllable.

__ān

__ān

__àn

__àn

h__

h__

h__

h__

二、听录音，标出声调
Listen to the recording and mark the tones.

wan bie zhang la jie zhang

三、听录音，选出你听到的音节
Listen to the recording and select the syllables you have heard.

cài	( )	zài	( )
fàng	( )	shàng	( )
méi	( )	gěi	( )
yào bié de	( )	yào bái de	( )
suānlàtāng	( )	suànleba	( )

四、听录音，按听到的顺序在相应的图下面写上序号
Listen to the recording and write down the sequence numbers below the corresponding pictures according to the order of what you have heard.

1.

一碗米饭	一壶花茶	一双筷子	一只烤鸭
( )	( )	( )	( )

2.

别放味精	结账	请给我一张餐巾纸	打包
( )	( )	( )	( )

五、听录音，选择正确答案
Listen to the recording and choose the correct answers.

1. A. 一把刀子　　B. 一把勺子
2. A. 宫保鸡丁　　B. 酸辣汤
3. A. 花茶　　B. 绿茶　　C. 啤酒

六、看汉字，写拼音
Look at the Chinese characters and write down the *pinyin* (the Chinese Phonetic Alphabet) for them.

茶　　碗　　菜　　米饭　　鸡丁　　结账

七、看拼音，用汉字写出句子
Look at the *pinyin* and write down the sentence using Chinese characters.

1. Yǎo yí gè gōngbǎo jīdīng.
2. Qǐng gěi wǒ yī zhāng cānjīnzhǐ.
3. Jiézhàng.

八. 选词填空
Fill in the blanks with the given words.

1. 斤 张 壶 个 双
   (1) 请给我一（　）餐巾纸。
   (2) 这（　）宫保鸡丁打包。
   (3) 一（　）饺子多少钱？
   (4) 小姐，我要一（　）花茶。
   (5) 再给我一（　）筷子，行吗？

2. 还 再 没 能 别
   (1) 我的菜怎么还（　）上？
   (2) 您（　）要别的吗？
   (3) 这个汤（　）放味精？
   (4)（　）要一个可乐。
   (5) 米饭（　）快点儿吗？

九、按正确的顺序把下面的词语排列成句
Arrange the following words into sentences in a proper ordered.

1. 一张　请　给　餐巾纸　我

______________________________。

2. 的　烤鸭　上　没　还　我们

______________________________。

十、选择合适的句子组成会话
Choose a proper sentence to complete each of the dialogues.

1. 服务员：这是菜单，请点菜。
   马丁：__________
   A. 要一只烤鸭。　B. 再要一碗米饭。

2. 服务员：您喝什么？
   马丁：__________
   A. 花茶呢？　B. 有啤酒吗？

3. 马丁：__________
   服务员：我去看看。
   A. 这个菜打包。　B. 我的菜能快点儿吗？

十一、完成下面的短文
Complete the following short passage.

到中国饭馆吃饭，我喜欢要__________，__________，再要__________，喝__________。我不喜欢吃__________，所以每次我都对服务员说："__________。"

十二、阅读并按要求答题
Read and answer the questions as requested.

1. 将下列句子排列成一段有意义的对话。Rearrange the following sentences to create a meaningful dialogue.

   ①我要一只烤鸭，再要一个麻婆豆腐。
   ②有什么？

③您喝什么？
④这是菜单，请点菜。
⑤有可乐、啤酒，还有花茶。
⑥我要一听可乐。

2. 阅读课堂活动第1部分第七题的菜单，回答问题。Read the menu in Exercise No.7, Part One of the Classroom Practice and answer the questions.

(1) 这个饭馆的特色菜有哪些？
(2) 热菜中，你喜欢的肉菜有哪些？
(3) 你喜欢的汤有哪些？
(4) 你喜欢的主食是什么？
(5) 你最喜欢喝的饮料是什么？
(6) 你觉得这个饭馆的菜贵不贵？

3. 阅读短文后填空。Fill in the blanks after reading the short passage.

中国 菜有 四大菜系 说、八大菜系 说，以 四大菜系 说 为 主。四大
Zhōngguó cài yǒu sìdàcàixì shuō, bādàcàixì shuō, yǐ sìdàcàixì shuō wéi zhǔ. Sìdà
菜系 是指 川菜、鲁菜、淮扬菜、粤菜。
càixì shì zhǐ Chuāncài, Lǔcài, Huáiyángcài, Yuècài.

川菜 就是 四川菜，主要 特点 是 麻辣。鲁菜 就是 山东菜，咸
Chuāncài jiù shì Sìchuāncài, zhǔyào tèdiǎn shì málà. Lǔcài jiù shì Shāndōng cài, xián
鲜 适口，南北 咸 宜，并 曾 大量 流入 宫廷。淮扬菜 最 大 的 特点
xiān shìkǒu, nánběi xián yí, bìng céng dàliàng liú rù gōngtíng. Huáiyángcài zuì dà de tèdiǎn
是 制作 精细。粤菜 就是 广东菜，突出 一个"杂"字，选材 广、奇，在
shì zhìzuò jīngxì. Yuècài jiù shì Guǎngdōngcài, tūchū yīgè "zá" zì, xuǎncái guǎng, qí, zài
做法 上 吸取 了 西餐 技艺。
zuòfǎ shàng xīqǔ le xīcān jìyì.

近 年 来，西式 快餐 在 中国 也 很 受 欢迎。例如 肯德基、麦当劳、
Jìn nián lái, xīshì kuàicān zài Zhōngguó yě hěn shòu huānyíng. Lìrú kěndéjī, Màidāngláo,
好伦哥、必胜客 等 西式 快餐厅，在 中国 的 大 城市 随处 可见。
Hǎolúngē, Bìshèngkè děng xīshì kuàicāntīng, zài Zhōngguó de dà chéngshì suíchù kějiàn.

(1) 填空：

麻辣是________的特点之一，咸鲜是________的特色，制作精细是______的最大特点，选材广泛、融合了西餐技艺的是________。

在中国比较常见的西式快餐有________、________、________、________等。

（2）看了上面的介绍，你最想吃的是哪一个菜系的菜？为什么？After reading the introduction above,which style of cooking would you like to have best?Why?

____

____

十三、数一数下列汉字的笔画，把笔画数写在下面

Count the strokes of the following Chinese Characters and write the numbers of stroke below.

请　菜　喝　账　鸡　汤　茶　纸

十四、按笔顺将下列汉字书写五遍

Write the following Chinese characters five times each, following the proper stroke order.

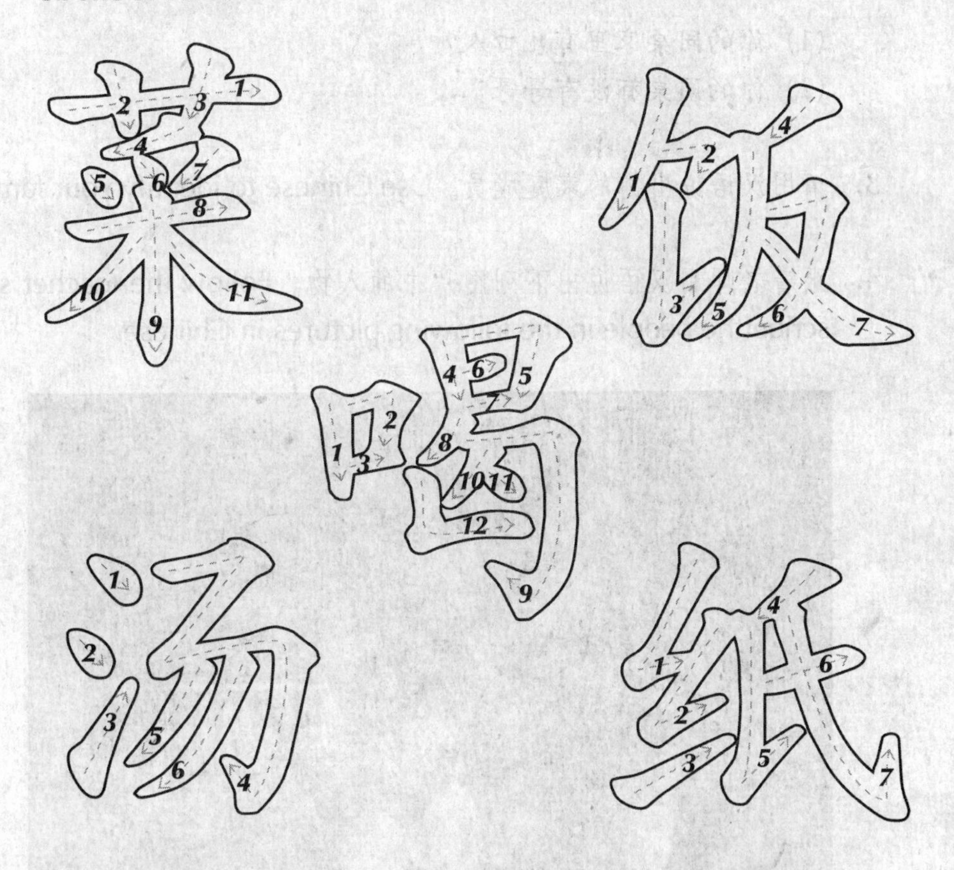

十五、实践活动：和朋友一起到中国饭馆点菜吃饭

Practice: Go to a Chinese restaurant with your friends and order some dishes.

Unit 5 你在哪儿工作？

课堂活动

第1部分

一、复习生词，学习亲属关系和职业的表达法

Review the new words and learn the expressions about family relations and professions.

1. 用汉语说出你对家人的称呼。What do you call your family members in Chinese.

2. 按下列要求问一问：Ask questions as requested.

   (1) 你的同桌家里有几口人？
   (2) 你的同桌有没有哥哥？

3. 请用汉语说出你的家庭成员。Use Chinese to identify your family members.

4. 跟着老师用汉语说出下列图片中的人物。Follow the teacher's lead and describe the people in the following pictures in Chinese.

5. 掌握下列表示亲属称谓关系的词。Please learn the the following words about the form of address in a family.

爷爷、奶奶　　哥哥、姐姐　　父亲、儿子

爸爸、妈妈　　弟弟、妹妹　　母亲、女儿　　丈夫、妻子

二、用汉语说出图中的称呼

Tell the form of address in the picture in Chinese.

三、两人一组，完成句子

Work in pairs, then identify the figures in the pictures and complete the sentences in Chinese.

这是我的妈妈，
她在医院工作，她是护士。

1. 这是我的_____，他在_____工作，他是_____。
2. 这是我的_____，她在_____工作，她是_____。
3. 这是我的_____，他在_____工作，他是_____。
4. 这是我的_____，她在_____工作，她是_____。

四、两人一组，仿照例句讨论你的家庭成员，然后完成表格

Work in pairs, and discuss your family members with the help of the example. Then, complete the form.

例：A：你家有几口人？

B：我家有四口人。

A：你家有什么人？

B：爸爸、妈妈、我和妹妹。

A：你爸爸在哪儿工作？

B：他在学校工作，他是老师。

A：你妈妈在哪儿工作？

B：她在医院工作，她是医生。

	我	同学
家里有几口人？		
家里有什么人？		
爸爸在哪儿工作？		
爸爸做什么工作？		
妈妈在哪儿工作？		
妈妈做什么工作？		
……		

五、看照片，两人一组互相问答

Look at the pictures and do the question-and-answer exercises with a partner.

1. 你家有几口人？
   你家有什么人？

2.

医生　教师　秘书　职员　厨师　司机　工人

你在哪儿工作？ ________________。

你做什么工作？ ________________。

六、根据下面的场景练习对话
Practise the dialogue according to the following situations.

(1) 饭店　　(2) 医院　　(3) 学校　　(4) 公司

A：你在哪儿工作？
B：我在＿＿＿＿。
A：你做什么工作？
B：我是＿＿＿＿。你呢？
B：我在＿＿＿＿，我是＿＿＿＿。

第2部分

一、请用汉语说出你的年龄
Please speak your age in Chinese.

二、根据实际情况回答问题
Answer the questions based on the practical situations.

问	答
1. 你今年多大？	我今年＿＿岁。
2. 你的同伴今年多大？	他（她）今年＿＿岁。
3. 你爸爸今年多大？	他今年＿＿岁。

三、两人一组，完成对话
Work in pairs and complete the dialogue.

A：她是谁？
B：她是我＿＿＿。
A：＿＿＿＿＿＿？
B：她今年二十六岁。
A：你今年多大？
B：＿＿＿＿＿＿。

四、两人一组，互相提问，完成下表
Complete the following form by asking each other questions in pairs.

问题	数字	
	我	同学
1. 你家有几口人		
2. 你有几个姐姐？		
3. 你有几个哥哥？		
4. 你爸爸多大年纪？		
5. 你妈妈多大年纪？		
6. ……		

五、两人一组，选择合适的词语完成对话
Choose suitable words to complete the dialogues in pairs.

几岁　多大年纪　多大

例： A：你姐姐今年多大？
　　B：她今年27岁。

(1) A：你儿子今年________？
　　B：他今年4岁。

(2) A：你哥哥今年________？
　　B：他今年30岁。

(3) A：你奶奶今年________？
　　B：我奶奶今年78岁。

六、用给出的汉语词语描述你的家人
Please use these Chinese words to describe your families.

我很________。

我哥哥很________。

我妈妈很________。

我爸爸很________。

我爷爷很________。

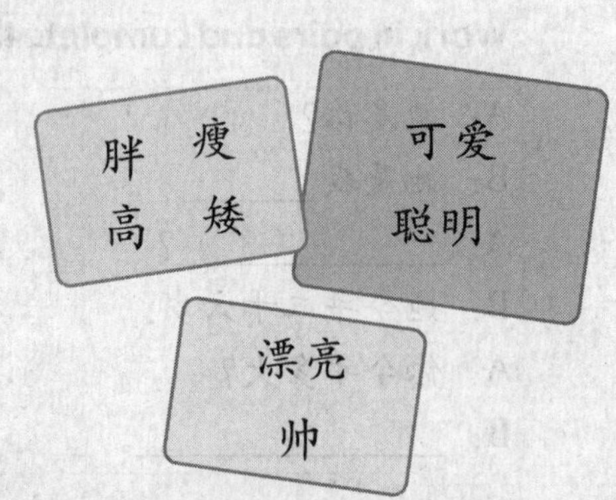

七、到班级里调查一下，完成下面的表格，然后和你的同伴对照一下答案是否一致

Conduct a survey in your class to complete the following form and then check with your partner to see whether your answers are consistent.

特　点	人　名
班里谁最高？	
班里谁最帅？	
班里谁最瘦？	
班里谁最漂亮？	
班里谁最聪明？	
班里谁最可爱？	

课后练习

一、听录音，填写声母或韵母

Listen to the recording and fill in the initial or the final sound of a syllable.

__ài
__ǒu
__ōng
__uí

j__
j__
j__
j__

二、听录音，标出声调
Listen to the recording and mark the tones.

ta　zuo　you　da　sui

三、听录音，选出你听到的音节
Listen to the recording and select the syllables you have heard.

mā	(　)	bà	(　)
shuí	(　)	shuài	(　)
zài	(　)	zuò	(　)
xué	(　)	jiě	(　)
suì	(　)	sì	(　)
cōng	(　)	gōng	(　)

四、听录音，选择正确的答案
Listen to the recording and choose the right answers.

1. 谁是说话人的爸爸？（ ）

男厨师
(A)

医生
(B)

画家
(C)

老师
(D)

2. 谁是说话人的妈妈？（ ）

3. 谁是说话人的姐姐？（ ）

高
(A)

矮
(B)

胖
(C)

瘦
(D)

五、听录音，选择正确答案
Listen to the recording and choose the right answers.

1. A. 十二岁 B. 二十岁

2. A. 护士 B. 医生

3. A. 三口 B. 四口

六、看汉字，写拼音
Look at the Chinese characters and write down the *pinyin* (the Chinese Phonetic Alphabet) for them.

他 和 谁 工作 老师

七、看拼音，用汉字写出句子
Look at the *pinyin* and write down the sentences using Chinese characters.

1. Wǒ jiā yǒu sì kǒu rén.

2. Tāmen shì shuí?

3. Nǐ jiā yǒu shénme rén?

八、根据提示完成任务
Complete the task as prompted.

(一) 用适当的亲属称谓词语填空Fill in the blanks using the appropriate form of family address.

1. Sam 是 Sophie 的 ______。Sophie 是 Sam 的 ______。
2. Peter 是 ______ 和 ______ 的儿子，是 Laura 的 ______，是 Lucy、Paul 和 Lily 的 ______。
3. Lucy 是 Peter 和 Laura 的 ______，是 Paul 和 ______ 的 ______。
4. Paul 是 Peter 和 Laura 的 ______，是 Lucy 的 ______，Lily 的 ______。
5. Lily 是 ______ 和 ______ 的女儿，是 Lucy 和 Paul 的 ______。

（二） 回答下列问题 Answer the following questions.

1. Sam 家有几口人？

____

2. Peter 在哪儿工作？

____

3. Laura 做什么工作？

____

4. Sam/Sophie 今年多大年纪？

____

5. Peter/Laura/Lucy/Paul 今年多大？

____

6. Lily 今年几岁？

____

九、连词成句

Make sentences by linking the words.

1. 哪儿 在 工作 你

______________________？

2. 我 四 人 家 有 口

______________________。

3. 哥哥 三十 我 岁

______________________。

十、回答下列问题
Answer the following questions.

1. 你多大了?

____

2. 你在哪儿工作?

____

3. 你家有几口人?

____

十一、完成下面的短文，然后读一读，并把它翻译成你的母语
Complete the following short passage, read it through and translate it into your native language.

我叫________，我今年______岁。我家有_____口人，________，________，________和我。我没有________。我爸爸今年_____岁，他在________工作，他是________________。我妈妈________________________。

十二、数一数下列汉字的笔画，把笔画数写在下面
Count the strokes of the following Chinese characters and write the numbers of stroke below.

口　　年　　岁　　哥　　作　　高

______　______　______　______　______　______

十三、找出下列每组汉字中相同的部件
Find the common component within each group of the following Chinese characters.

例：后　回　号　听　　（口）

1. 你　他　们　做　　（　　）　　2. 妈　姐　妹　奶　　（　　）

十四、用以下词语造句
Make sentences using the following words.

哪儿 ________________________________

什么 ________________________________

谁 ________________________________

多大 ______

几岁 ______

多大年纪 ______

几口人 ______

几个 ______

十五、阅读这段文章，然后找出里面所有的职业名称
Read this passage, identify each profession.

我家有八口人，爷爷、奶奶、爸爸、妈妈、哥哥、姐姐、弟弟和我，是
Wǒ jiā yǒu bā kǒu rén, yéye, nǎinai, bàba, māma, gēge, jiějie, dìdi hé wǒ, shì
一个很大的家庭。爷爷以前是医生，现在他不工作了，他想让
yí gè hěn dà de jiātīng. Yéye yǐqián shì yīshēng, xiànzài tā bù gōng zuò lē, tā xiǎng ràng
我姐姐当护士。奶奶以前是会计，在一家小公司工作。我爸爸大学
wǒ jiějie dāng hùshì. Nǎinai yǐqián shì kuàijì, zài yì jiā xiǎo gōng sī gōngzuò.Wǒ bàba dàxué
毕业以后，没有到医院工作，他做了律师。我妈妈现在是公司的
bìyè yǐ hòu, méiyǒu dào yīyuàn gōngzuò,tā zuò lē lǜshī. Wǒ māma xiànzài shì gōngsī de
秘书，我哥哥也在那个公司当保安，我姐姐在饭店工作，是
mìshū, wǒ gēge yě zài nàgē gōngsī dāng bǎoān, wǒ jiějie zài fàndiàn gōngzuò, shì
服务员。我现在是公司职员，可是我的梦想是在大使馆当
fúwùyuán. Wǒxiànzài shì gōngsī zhíyuán, kěshì wǒ de mèngxiǎng shì zài dàshǐguǎn dāng
大使。我的弟弟想当出租车司机。这就是我的家庭。
dàshǐ. Wǒ de dìdi xiǎng dāng chūzūchē sījī. Zhè jiù shì wǒ de jiātíng.

十六、实践活动：给每个家庭成员写一个介绍
Practice: Introduce each of your family members.

例：姐姐

我姐姐叫珍妮，她今年23岁。她在公司上班，她是公司职员。她很漂亮。

Unit 6 珍妮在吗？

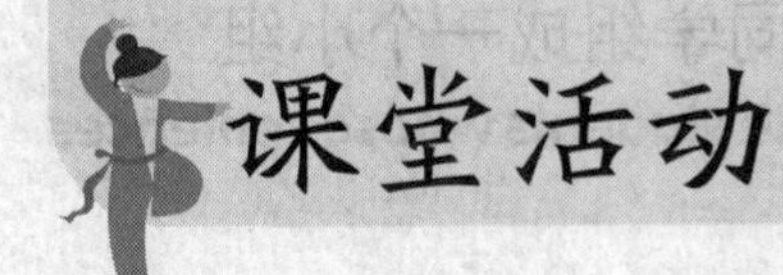

课堂活动

第 1 部分

一、根据要求完成任务
Complete the tasks as requested.

1. 用汉语说出你知道的通讯方式。Use Chinese to describe the methods of communication you know of.

2. 跟老师用汉语说出下图内容。Describe the following pictures to the teacher in Chinese.

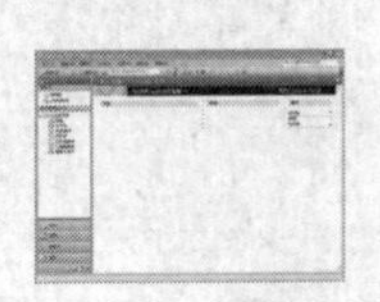

3. 用汉语说出你最常用的通讯方式。Tell us your most frequently used way of communication in Chinese.

二、看图完成句子
Look at the picture and complete the sentences.

1. 我找________。他在吗？
2. ________在不在？
3. 是________吗？
4. ________在吗？

三、两人一组，看图完成对话
Look at the picture and complete the dialogues with a partner.

1. A：我找王华。他在吗？
   B：____________________。
2. A：王华在不在？
   B：____________________。

3. A：是王华吗？

   B：________________。

四、每人抽一句话，找出和你的句子意思相同的同学组成一个小组

Each student draws a sentence. Then form groups, with students whose sentences have the same meaning grouping together.

是王先生吗？	宋丽丽在不在？
你买苹果吗？	是不是王先生？
宋丽丽在吗？	他是不是老师？
你是中国人吗？	能不能快点儿？
她是你姐姐吗？	你哥哥帅不帅？
你哥哥帅吗？	放不放味精？
这件大吗？	你买不买苹果？
他是老师吗？	这件大不大？
放味精吗？	她是不是你姐姐？
能快点儿吗？	你是不是中国人？

五、按刚组成的小组完成对话

Complete the dialogue based on the grouping above.

A：喂！你好！

B：__________ 您找谁？

A：____________ 在吗？

B：________________

第2部分

一、按要求回答

Answer the questions as requested.

1. 你每天都去哪些地方？ Which places do you visit every day?

2. 你最喜欢去什么地方？ Which place do you enjoy visiting best?

二、看图完成对话

Look at the picture and complete the dialogue.

A：__________在不在？

B：他/她去__________了。

三、两人一组，为下面的问题找出尽可能多的应答语

Work in pairs, then find as many replies as possible for the following questions.

问	答
喂！您找谁？	
喂！你好！李小姐在吗？	

四、四人一组，每人抽取一个句子，然后组成一个对话

Form groups of four people. Each person should draw a sentence, then make a dialogue accordingly.

A. 在，请稍等。

B. 喂！你好！请问，张华在吗？

C. 我是王老师。

D. 喂！你好！我是张华。您哪位？

五、两人一组，完成对话

Work in pairs and complete the following dialogue.

A：喂！你好！

B：喂！ ________________

A：请问，__________ 在吗？

B：________________。您哪位？

A：我是他/她的 ______________。请他/她回来后给我回电话。

B：您的电话是多少？

A：________________。

六、两人一组，设计一段打电话的情景，并表演出来

Work in pairs and create and perform a scene involving the making of calls.

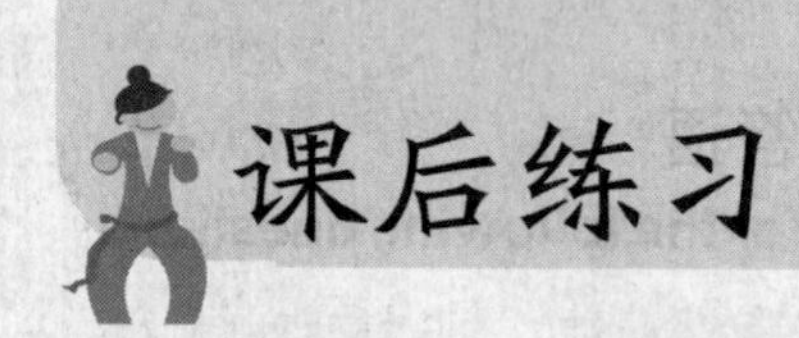

课后练习

一、听录音，填写声母或韵母

Listen to the recording and fill in the initial or the final sound of a syllable.

__ěng

__éng

__ǎo

__āo

w__

w__

d__

d__

二、听录音，标出声调

Listen to the recording and mark the tones.

jiu zhao cuo gei hua qing ta shao

三、听录音，选出你听到的音节
Listen to the recording and check(✓) the syllables you have heard.

xíng	(　)	qǐng	(　)
shāo	(　)	zhǎo	(　)
cuò	(　)	zuò	(　)
tā	(　)	fā	(　)
chéng	(　)	péng	(　)
dǎ	(　)	dà	(　)
jiù	(　)	jiǔ	(　)
diànhuà	(　)	huāchá	(　)

四、听录音，选出你听到的句子
Listen to the recording and select the sentences you have heard.

1. 您找谁？　　您哪位？
2. 他去商店了。　　他去饭店了。
3. 马丁在不在？　　马丁不在。
4. 我是他的姐姐张华。　　我是他的朋友张华。

五、听录音，选择合适的应答语组成会话
Listen to the recording and select the suitable replies to make up dialogues.

1. (　)

A. 张华在吗？
B. 我是张华。
C. 你好！

2. (　)

A. 我找马丁。
B. 我是马丁。
C. 马丁不在。

3. (　)

A. 她不在。
B. 她去学校了。
C. 我就是。

六、听录音，判断正误

Listen to the recording and judge what you heard is right or wrong.

1. 男的给女的打电话。 （ ）
2. 男的姓王。 （ ）
3. 女的叫李华。 （ ）
4. 女的是一位老师。 （ ）
5. 男的有个女儿。 （ ）

七、根据拼音写出两个同音字

Write out two homophones according to the *pinyin*.

1. tā （ ） （ ）
2. wèi （ ） （ ）
3. diàn （ ） （ ）
4. shì （ ） （ ）

八、选词填空

Fill in the blanks with the correct words.

就 位 错 找 给 在
1. 喂！你（ ）谁？
2. 请问张华（ ）吗？
3. 我（ ）是张华。
4. 请问您哪（ ）？
5. 对不起，你打（ ）了。
6. 请他（ ）我回电话。

九、把括号里的词语填在句中适当的位置

Put the words in brackets into the suitable places in the sentences.

1. ____马丁____在____在____？ （不）
2. ____我____是____马丁____。 （就）
3. ____他____去____银行____。 （了）
4. 我____是____他____朋友____。 （的）

十、回答问题

Answer the questions.

1. 你的电话是多少？

   ______________________________。

2. 现在你爸爸在家吗？

   ______________________________。

3. 现在你家谁不在？去哪儿了？

   ______________________________。

十一、完成对话

Complete the dialogue in your own way.

A：喂！你好！

B：喂！______________________

A：张华______________________

B：______________________

十二、阅读并回答问题

Read and answer the questions.

丽丽：

下午3：30你的朋友马丁给你打电话，你去银行了。马丁请你给他回电话，他的电话是65323665。

妈妈

6月16日

1. 这是谁给谁留的便条？

   ______________________________。

2. 谁给谁打电话？几点打的？

   ______________________________。

3. 丽丽下午去哪儿了？

   ______________________________。

4. 马丁请丽丽做什么？

   ______________________________。

5. 马丁的电话是多少？

________________________。

6. 根据教材第二部分的会话，仿写便条。

十三、按笔画数由少到多排列汉字
Arrange the Chinese characters in the order of ascending numbers of stroke.

喂 找 打 错 问 朋 友 给

十四、将下面的部件组合成你学过的汉字
Combine the following parts into the Chinese characters you have learnt.

例： 扌＋丁→打

门 月 戈 口 扌 月 亻 立 乍 十 攵

①____ ②____ ③____ ④____ ⑤____ ⑥____ ⑦____

十五、按笔顺将下列汉字书写五遍
Write the following Chinese characters five times each, following the proper stroke order.

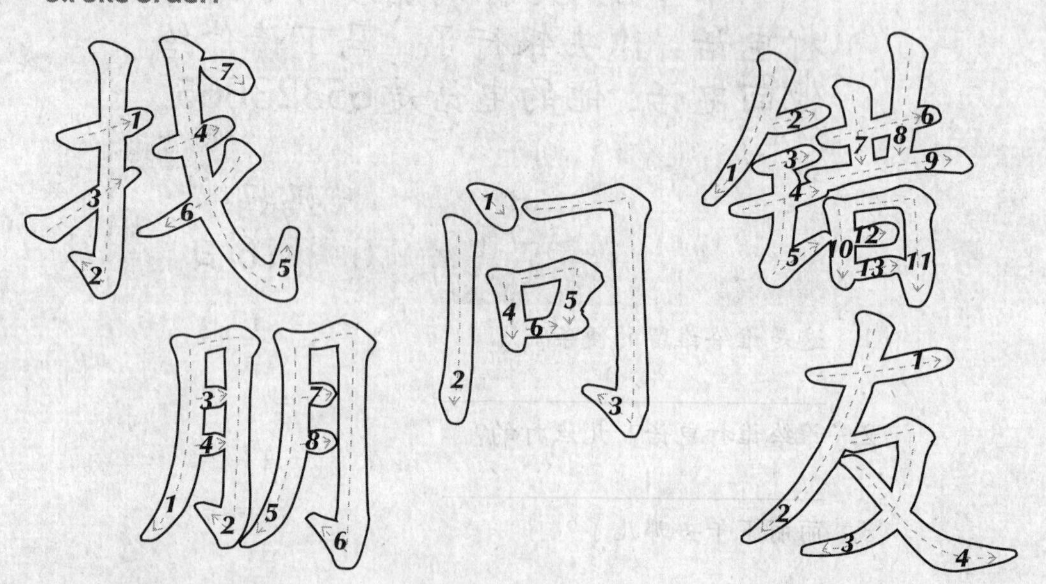

十六、实践活动：给一个中国朋友打电话，问问他／她的家庭情况
Practice: Call a Chinese friend to ask about his/her family situation.

Unit 7 一直走

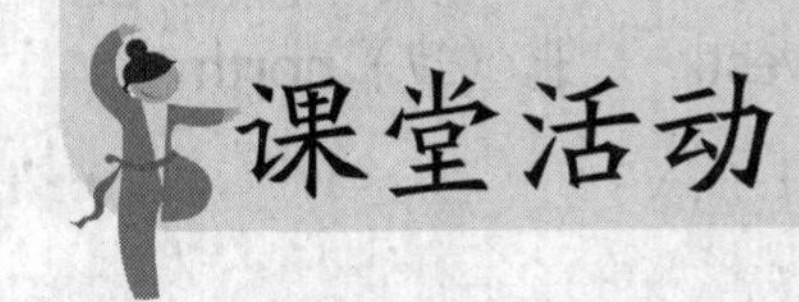

课堂活动

第1部分

一、复习表示方位的名词，学习方位表达法

Review the nouns that indicate orientation and learn the expressions of orientation.

1. 用汉语说出你所知道的表示方位的名词。Pronounce the nouns of orientation that you know in Chinese.

2. 按下列要求说一说：Speak according to the following requests:

   (1) 你的前边是谁？后边呢？左边呢？右边呢？
   (2) 谁在你的东边？南边呢？西边呢？北边呢？
   (3) 你的东北边是谁？东南边呢？西北边呢？西南边呢？
   (4) 你坐在教室的哪个方位？

3. 请用汉语说出你的故乡在你的国家的哪个方位。Use Chinese to identify the part of your country in which your hometown is located.

4. 跟老师用汉语说出下列图示的方位。Use Chinese to give the teacher the directions shown in the following pictures.

5. 掌握下列表示方位的名词。Please learn the following nouns that indicate orientation.

前（边）front	后（边）back	左（边）left	右（边）right
东（边）east	南（边）south	西（边）west	北（边）north

二、用汉语说出图中人物所在的方位

Use Chinese to pronounce the nouns that indicate orientation in the picture.

三、看图完成句子

Look at the pictures and complete the sentences.

1. 去<u>大众公司</u>怎么走？	2. 一直走，然后往<u>右</u>拐。	3. 到<u>红绿灯</u>往右拐。
饭店	左	第二个十字路口
商店	东	丁字路口
学校	北	人行横道
医院	南	过街天桥
银行	西	立交桥

四、两人一组，根据地图问路、指路

Work in pairs, then ask and direct the way based on the map.

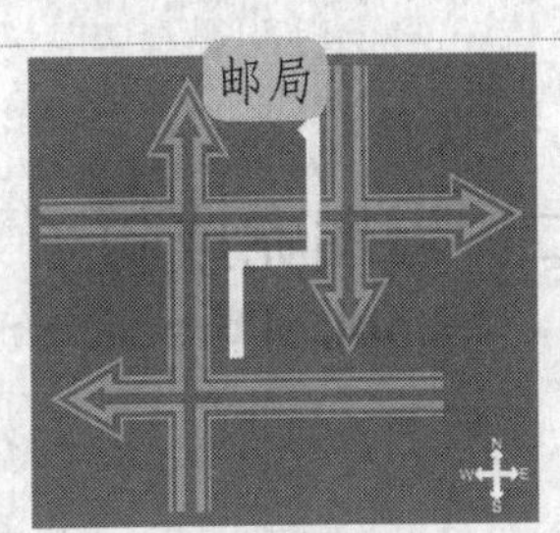

例：A：到学校怎么走？

B：一直走，到红绿灯往左拐。

五、两人一组，选用下面的句式和词语对话。要求：问路人把听到的路线画出来，然后给指路人看，看谁画得又快又准

Work in pairs and use the following sentence patterns and words to make a dialogue. The person asking the way draws the route he/she heard about and shows it to the person giving directions. Find out who is the quickest and most accurate draughtsman.

去……怎么走？	左	右	东
一直走。	南	西	北
往……拐。	红绿灯	十字路口	丁字路口
到……往……拐。	立交桥	过街天桥	人行横道

第2部分

一、交通工具

Transportation vehicle

1. 请用汉语说出下列交通工具的名称。Use Chinese to pronounce the names of the following transportation vehicles.

2. 请用汉语说出乘坐上题中交通工具的表达法。Use Chinese to pronounce the expressions of travelling by the above-mentioned transportation vehicles.

二、看图完成句子

Look at the pictures and complete the sentences.

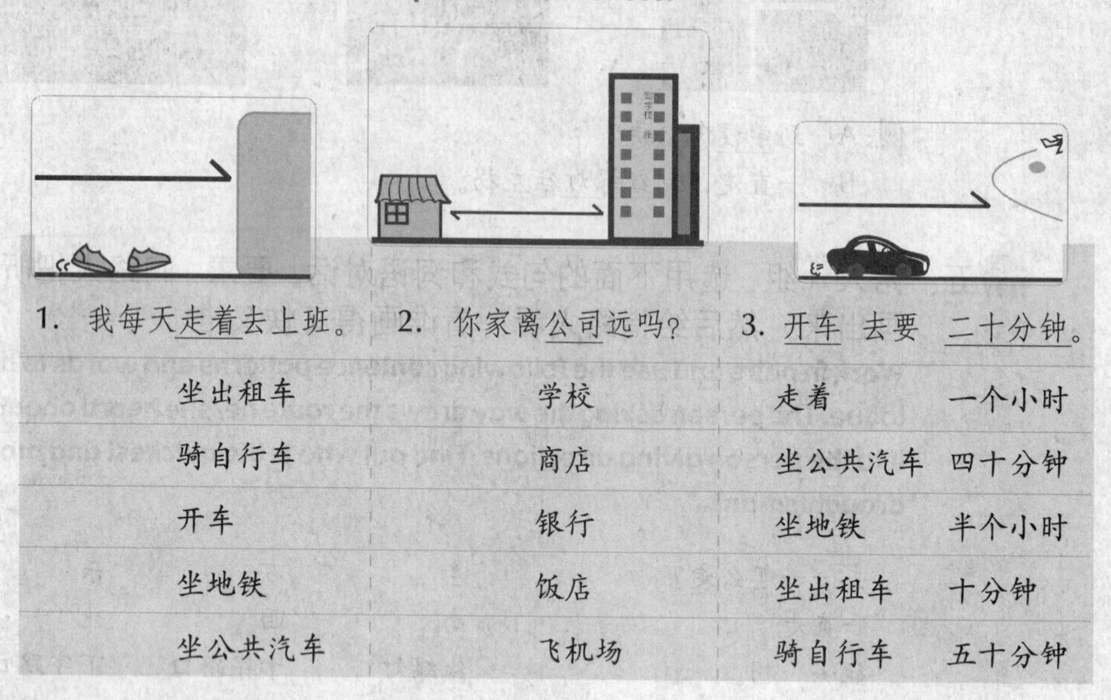

1. 我每天走着去上班。 2. 你家离公司远吗？ 3. 开车 去要 二十分钟。

坐出租车	学校	走着	一个小时
骑自行车	商店	坐公共汽车	四十分钟
开车	银行	坐地铁	半个小时
坐地铁	饭店	坐出租车	十分钟
坐公共汽车	飞机场	骑自行车	五十分钟

三、两人一组，完成对话

Work in pairs and complete the dialogue.

A：你每天怎么去学校？

B：______去。

A：你家离学校远吗？

B：不远，______去要______。

A：为什么不______？

B：我怕______。

四、两人一组，按照下列句式，互相提问，完成下表

Work in pairs,then complete the following form by using the following sentence patterns to ask by using each other questions.

	去哪儿	怎么去	远　吗	多长时间
A				
B				

提示语： A：你去哪儿？
B：我去……。
A：你怎么去……？
B：……去。
A：……离这儿远吗？
B：……，……要……。

图书城
游泳馆
咖啡厅

五、在纸上写下3个你常去的地方，然后两人一组谈谈交通工具

Work in pairs. Write down three places that you often visit and then talk about by what transportation vehicles you would like to go.

例： 甲：你怎么去______？
乙：______去。
甲：______离你家远吗？
乙：______，______去要______。

六、两人一组选用下面的句式和词语对话

Work in pairs and choose the following sentence patterns and words to make up dialogues.

你怎么去……？	公司	上班	学校
……离……远吗？	使馆	银行	飞机场
……去。	开车	走着	坐公共汽车
……去要……。	坐地铁	骑自行车	坐出租车

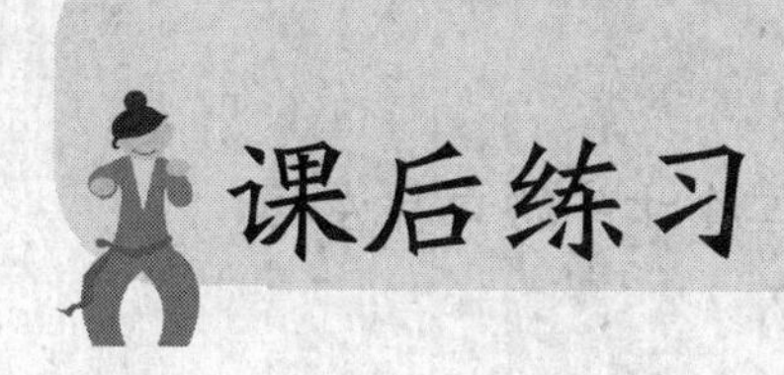

课后练习

一、听录音，填写声母或韵母

Listen to the recording and fill in the initial or the final sound of a syllable.

__ǒu
__ào
__ōng
__ī

l__
g__
z__

二、听录音，标出声调
Listen to the recording and mark the tones.

shang xing kai tie yuan

三、听录音，选出你听到的音节
Listen to the recording and select the syllables you have heard.

xué ( ) xié ( )
guǎi ( ) gǎi ( )
piāo ( ) biāo ( )
sī ( ) shī ( )
fēn ( ) fēng ( )
yāo ( ) yào ( )

四、听录音，用不同的符号（如＊ △ @）分别标出学校、商店、公司的位置
Listen to the recording and mark separately the locations of the school, shop and company using different signs (like ＊ △ @).

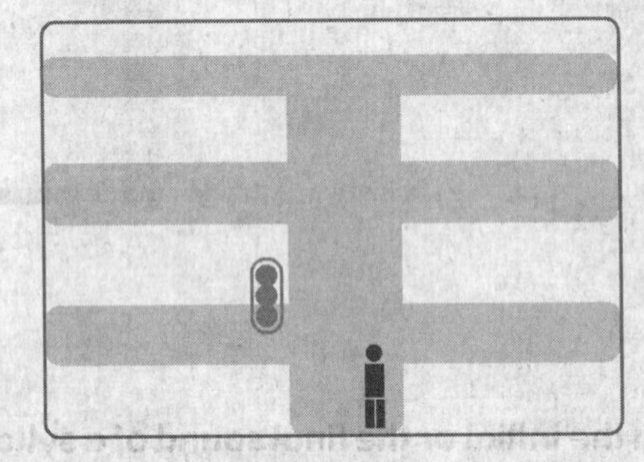

A：学校怎么走？
B：一直走，第二个十字路口往左拐。
A：商店怎么走？
B：一直走，到红绿灯往右拐。
A：公司怎么走？
B：一直走，到丁字路口往右拐。

五、听录音，选择正确答案
Listen to the recording and choose the right answers.

1. A. 坐出租车　　B. 骑自行车

2. A. 不近　　B. 很近

3. A. 二十分钟　　B. 半个小时

六、看汉字，写拼音
Look at the Chinese characters and write down the pinyin (the Chinese Phonetic Alphabet) for them.

拐　　红绿灯　　发票　　堵车

七、看拼音，用汉字写出句子
Look at the *pinyin* and write down the sentences using Chinese characters.

1. Nǐ zhīdào qù nǎr zěnme zǒu ma?

2. Wèishénme bù kāichē?

八、连词成句
Make sentences by linking the words.

1. 哪儿 你 去

_______________________________________?

2. 怎么 去 你家 走

_______________________________________。

3. 去 十五 要 分钟 坐 出租车

_______________________________________。

九、回答下列问题
Answer the following questions.

1. 去医院怎么走？

____

2. 你怎么去飞机场？

____

3. 飞机场离你家很远吗？

____

十、完成下面的短文
Complete the following short passage.

我每天______去学校，学校离我家______，______要十分钟。一直走，到______往右拐。我不______，我怕______。

十一、假如一个人要坐出租车去飞机场，可是不知道怎么走，用下面的句式写出可能发生的对话
A person wants to take a taxi to the airport but does not know the way.Make a dialogue using the following sentence patterns.

A. 您去哪儿？
B. 一直走，到……往……拐。

A. 你知道……吗？
B. ……离这儿远吗？

A. 去……怎么走？
B. ……去要……。

十二、数一数下列汉字的笔画，把笔画数写在下面
Identify the common components within each of the following groups of Chinese characters.

车	直	停	分	堵	着
______	______	______	______	______	______

十三、找出下列每组汉字中相同的部件
Find out the same parts within each group of the following Chinese characters.

例：后 回 号 （口）

1. 道 这 近 （ ）
2. 很 行 往 （ ）
3. 你 停 件 （ ）

十四、按笔顺将下列汉字书写五遍

Write the following Chinese characters five times each, following the proper stroke order.

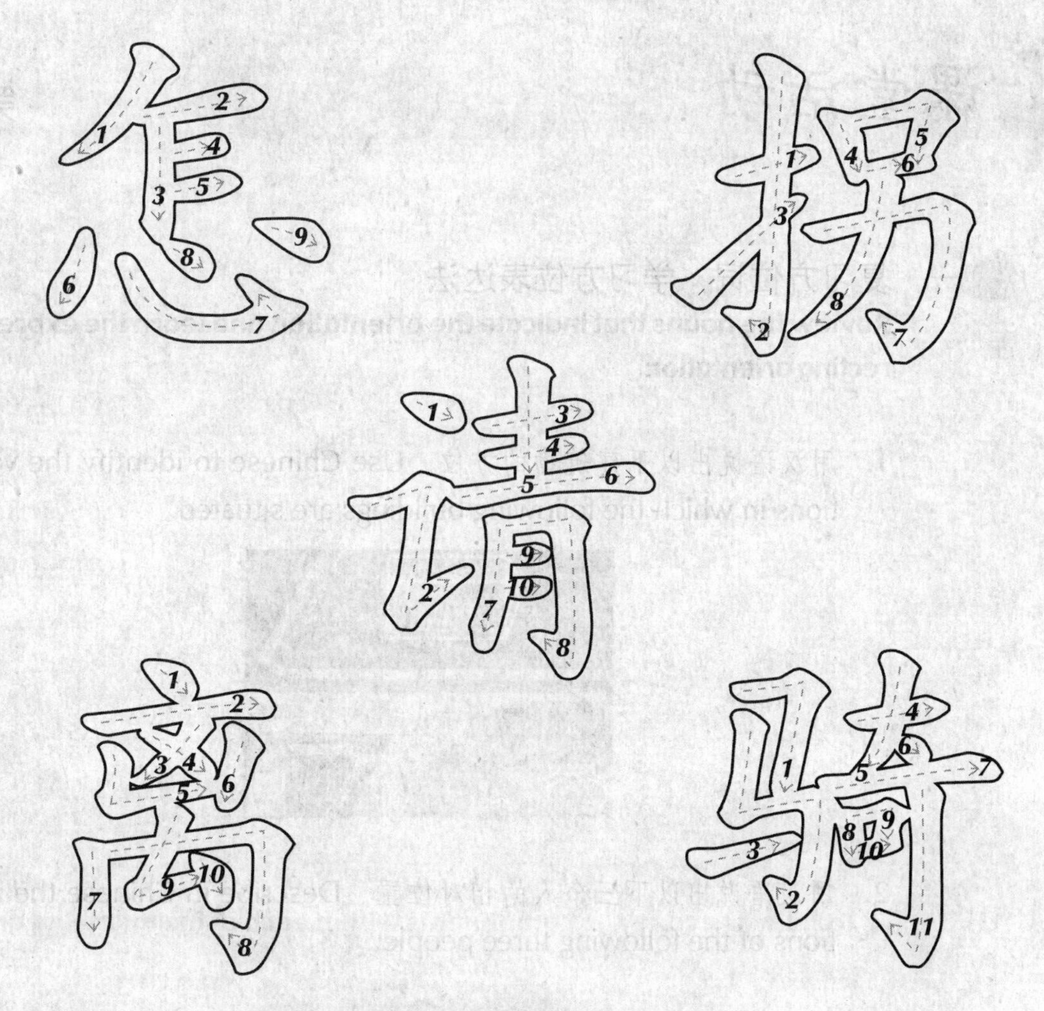

十五、实践活动：制作一个去学校、商店、医院、银行的路线图，并用汉语说出来

Practice: Draw a map giving the routes to the school, shop, hospital and bank, then explain them in Chinese.

Unit 8 你的新家在哪儿？

课堂活动

第1部分

一、复习方位词，学习方位表达法

Review the nouns that indicate the orientation and learn the expressions of directing orientation.

1. 用汉语说出以下建筑物的方位。Use Chinese to identify the various directions in which the following buildings are situated.

2. 用汉语说出以下三个人的相对位置。Describe in Chinese the relative positions of the following three people.

3. 说说下列图中小老鼠的相对位置。Describe the relative positions of the little mouse in the following pictures.

小老鼠在哪儿？

4. 请根据教室里的情况，回答下面的问题。Please answer the following questions according to the situation in the classroom.

(1) 老师在哪儿？ (4) 你的书在哪儿？
(2) 学生在哪儿？ (5) 你的笔在哪儿？
(3) 电脑在哪儿？ (6) 你的本子在哪儿？

二、复习课文句型，熟练方位表达

Review the sentence patterns of the text and familiarize yourself with the expressions of orientation.

1. 根据下图，仿照例子和老师或同学对话。注意用“左边、右边、上边、下边、中间”。Follow the example given in the picture, and talk with the teacher or a classmate. Use the words “left, right, up, down, middle”.

例： A：我的字典呢？
B：什么字典？
A：《新华字典》。
B：在桌子上吗？
A：我找了，没有。
B：啊。在书架上。在中间那层书的上面。

2. 请跟老师用汉语回答下面的问题。Please follow the teacher's lead to answer the following questions speak in Chinese.

(1) 钱放在哪里最安全？
(2) 手机放在哪里最方便？
(3) 电视放在哪里最好？
(4) 小汽车停在哪里最放心？

3. 藏起你的一件小物品，请老师和同学猜猜这件东西在哪里。请使用以下句型：Hide one of your belongings and ask the teacher and classmates to guess where it is. Please use the following sentence patterns.

A：我的钥匙呢？
B：在……吗？
A：不在。
B：在……吗？
A：……

4. 图中的卧室要放入以下物品：床、桌子、电视、冰箱、衣柜。请两人一组做出一个最合理的布置方案。并向老师和其他同学描述你布置好的房间。
The following objects need to be placed in the bedroom in the picture: bed, table, TV set, refrigerator,and wardrobe. Please form pairs to create a reasonable decoration plan,then describe it to the teacher and your other classmates.

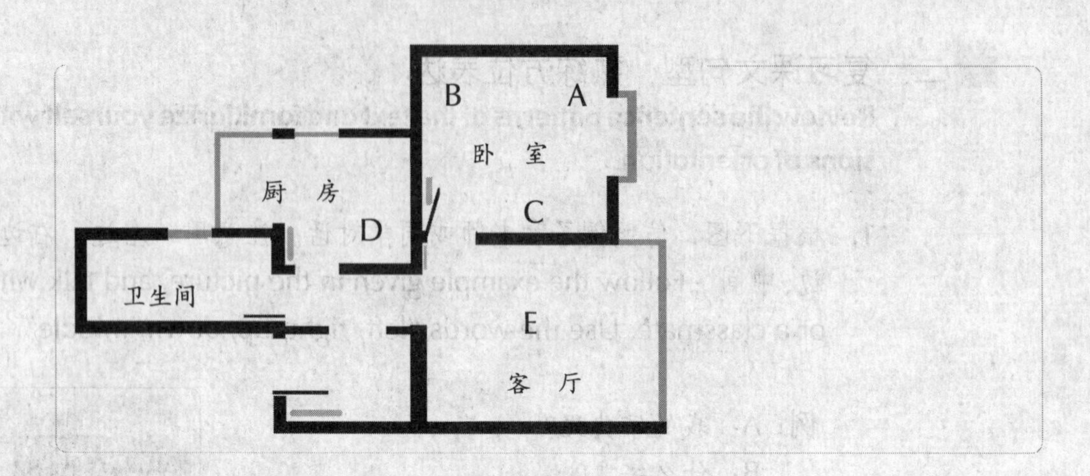

第2部分

一、跟老师说说图片中东西的位置
Discuss the locations of the various items in the picture with your teacher.

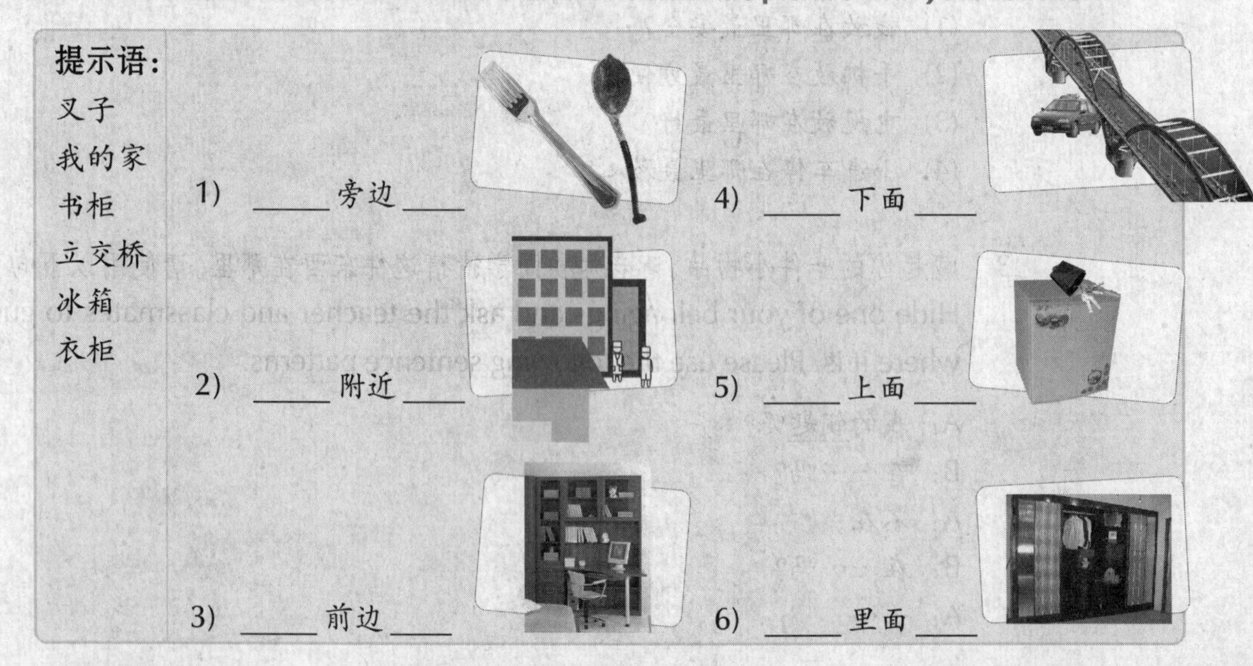

二、仿照例子描述教室里的物品（注意把句子连起来）

Follow the example to describe the objects in the classroom.(Make sure you link the sentences properly)

例：教室里面有一张桌子。桌子旁边有一位老师。老师前面有六个学生。

三、仿照例子改写句子

Follow the example to rewrite the sentence.

例1： 盘子里面有一双筷子。→筷子在盘子里面。

(1) 银行外面有一辆自行车。→ ______________________。

(2) 椅子上面有一本书。 → ______________________。

(3) 餐巾纸下面有一张菜单。→ ______________________。

(4) 大使馆附近有一家饭店。→ ______________________。

(5) 超市后面有一家医院。→ ______________________。

例2： 钥匙在桌子下面。→桌子下面有一把钥匙。

(1) 饭馆在飞机场对面。 → ______________________。

(2) 红绿灯在车站旁边。 → ______________________。

(3) 手机在衣柜里面。 → ______________________。

(4) 椅子在冰箱和桌子中间。→ ______________________。

(5) 刀子在菜单右边。 → ______________________。

四、仿照下面格式，按照你的实际情况和同学完成对话。方框中的内容可替换。左边是替换举例。

Follow the following format to complete the dialogue with your classmate according to your practical situation. The contents in the square frame can be replaced. And, example of such replacement can be found on the left.

A：听说你搬家了。
B：对，原来的房子太小了。
A：你的新家在哪儿？

转学……
原来的学校太远了……
新学校……

B：在朝阳公园旁边。
A：那儿怎么样？
B：很漂亮。马路对面有一个公园，附近还有一个大超市。

在大使馆旁边……
学校对面有一家商店……
附近还有一家医院……

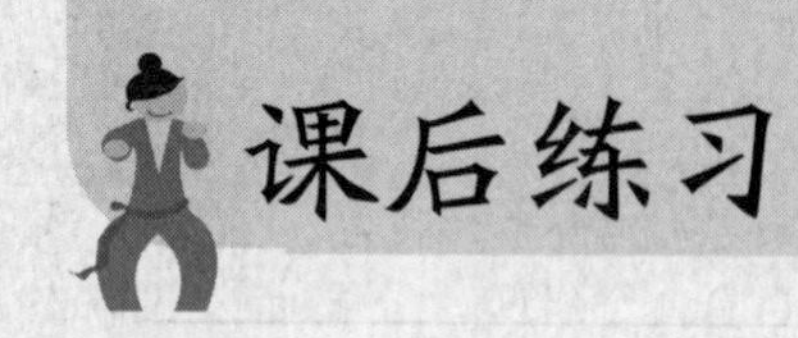

课后练习

一、听录音，填写声母或韵母
Listen to the recording and fill in the initial or the final sound of a syllable.

__àng
__áng
__áng

x__
x__
x__

二、听录音，标出声调
Listen to the recording and mark the tones.

yuan　yang　chao　shi　ting

三、听录音，选出你听到的音节
Listen to the recording and select the syllables you have heard.

pēi　(　)　　bēi　(　)
jī　(　)　　qī　(　)
xì　(　)　　jì　(　)
zhēn　(　)　　zhēng　(　)
sè　(　)　　zè　(　)
fū　(　)　　hū　(　)

四、听录音，按听到的顺序在相应的图下面写上序号

Listen to the recording and write down the sequence numbers below the corresponding picture according to the order of what you have heard.

1. ( ) ( ) ( ) ( )

2. ( ) ( ) ( ) ( )

五、听录音，选择正确答案

Listen to the recording and choose the right answers.

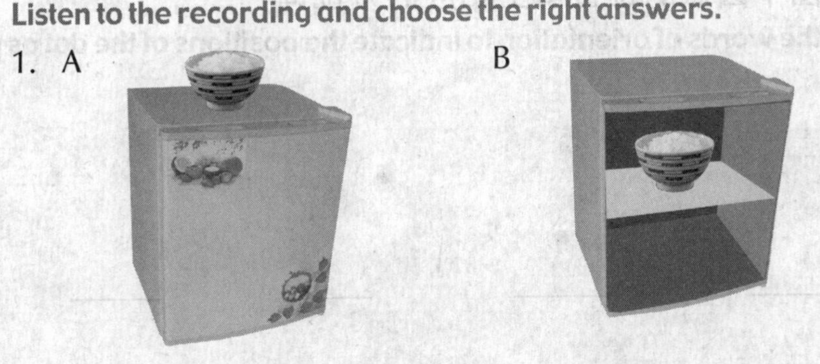

1. A B

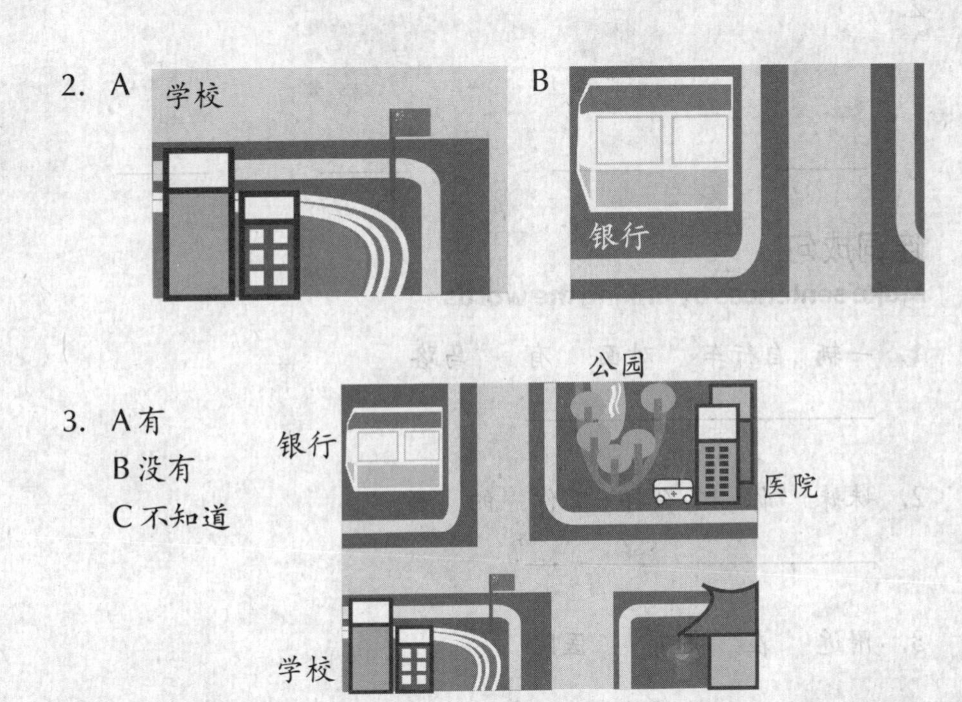

2. A B

3. A 有
   B 没有
   C 不知道

六、看汉字，写拼音

Look at the Chinese characters and write down the *pinyin* (the Chinese Phonetic Alphabet) for them.

夫人　　杂志　　原来　　搬家

七、看拼音，用汉字写出句子

Look at the *pinyin* and write down the sentences using Chinese characters.

1. Wǒde xīnjiā zài fēijīchǎng fùjìn.

2. Shūguìlǐ yǒu yīběn hóngsède zhōngwénshū.

八、根据图中圆点的位置填上相应的方位词

Fill in the words of orientation to indicate the positions of the dot as prompted.

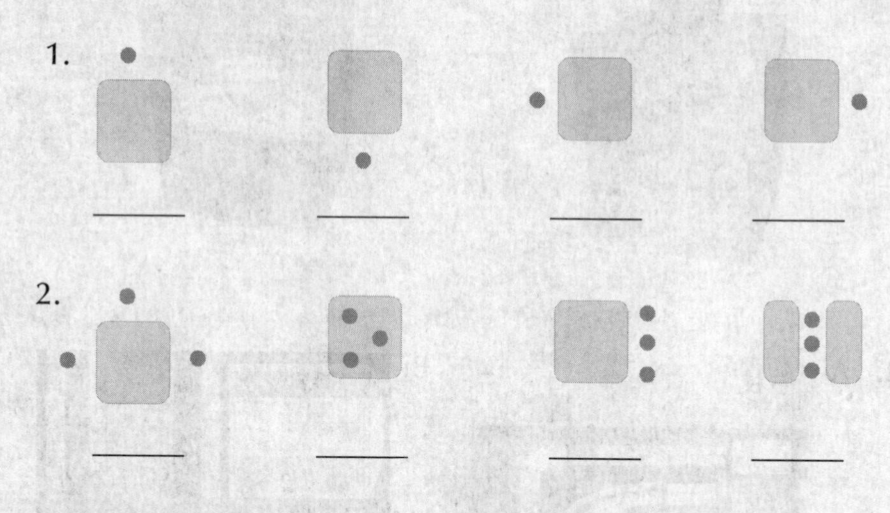

九、连词成句

Make sentences by linking the words.

1. 一辆　自行车　对面　有　马路

______________________。

2. 妹妹　你　怎么样　工作　的　新

______________________？

3. 附近　在　超市　医院

______________________。

十、回答下列问题

Answer the following questions.

1. 你家在哪儿？

____

2. 你家附近有什么？

____

3. 你的房子怎么样？

____

十一、请把下面一段文字翻译成汉语

Please translate the following passage into chinese.

I've moved house. My parents both work for the American Embassy. Our new home is located near the Embassy and in a huge apartment building. The apartment is nice and also convenient. There is a bank and a hospital opposite the road. There is a Chinese restaurant beside the hospital. I like the dishes of this restaurant very much.

十二、用方位词说话

Talk with words of orientation.

1. 熟悉下面方位词。Familiarize yourself with the following words of orientation.

东边、西边、南边、北边、东北边、东南边、西北边、西南边

2. 请说出下列各国的方位。Answer the following questions.

(1) 美国在加拿大的什么方位？

(2) 中国在日本的什么方位？

(3) 英国在法国的什么方位？德国在西班牙的什么方位？

十三、看图并回答问题
Read and answer the questions.

下面是北京大学校园地图的一部分，请按此图回答问题。
Below is part of the Peking University campus map.Please answer the questions according to this map.

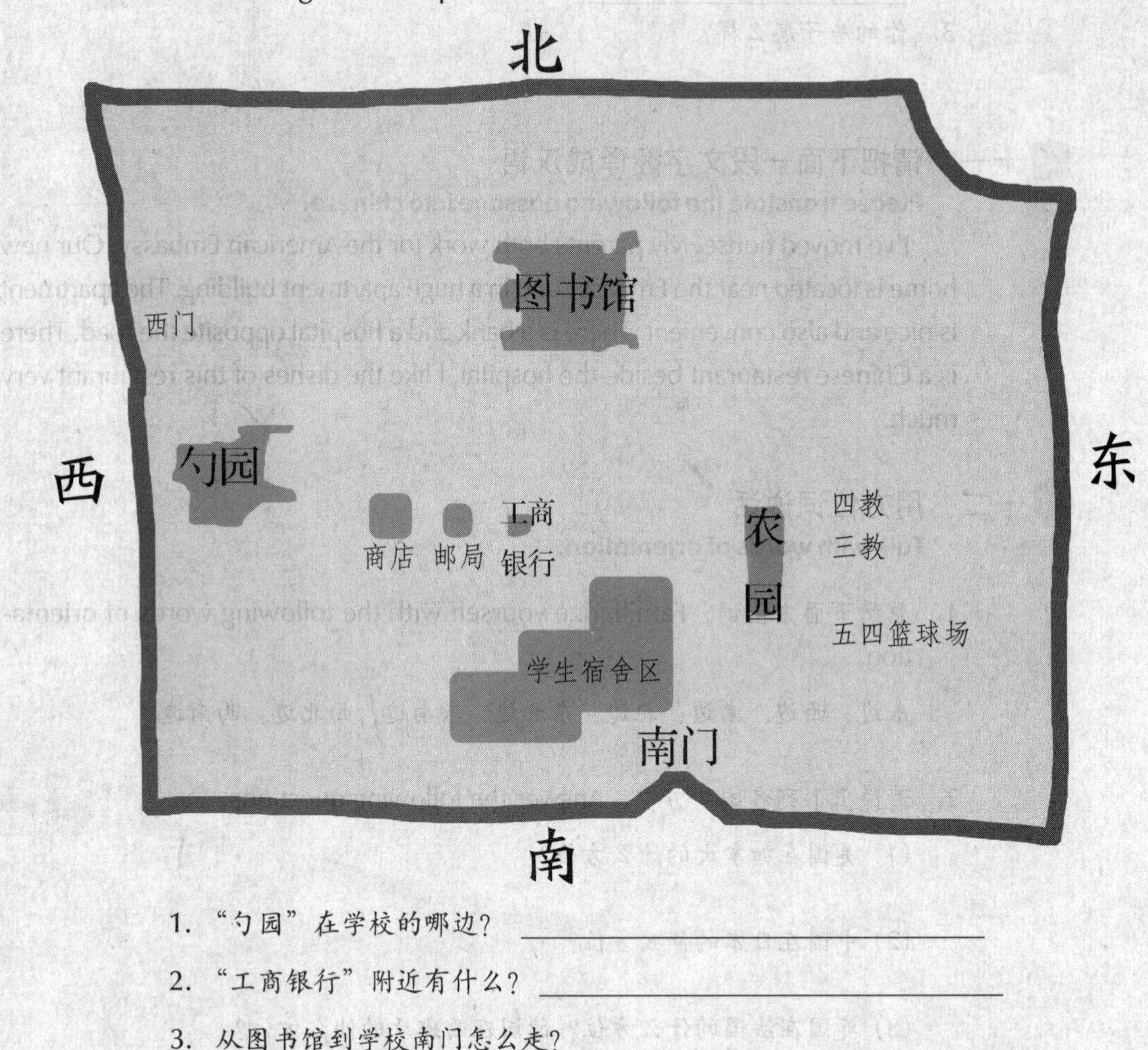

1. “勺园”在学校的哪边？______
2. “工商银行”附近有什么？______
3. 从图书馆到学校南门怎么走？______
4. “农园”的东边有什么？______
5. 如果要开一家学生酒吧，应该建在哪里？为什么？

______

______

十四、数一数下列汉字的笔画，把笔画数写在下面

Count the strokes of the following Chinese characters and write the number of strokes below.

对　　旁　　边　　本　　里　　亮

_____　_____　_____　_____　_____　_____

十五、找出下列每组汉字中相同的部件

Identify the common components within each of the following groups of Chinese characters.

例：后　回　号　（口）

1. 椅　柜　样　（　　）
2. 饭　馆　饺　（　　）
3. 箱　筷　笔　（　　）

十六、按笔顺将下列汉字书写五遍

Write the following Chinese characters five times each, following the proper stroke order.

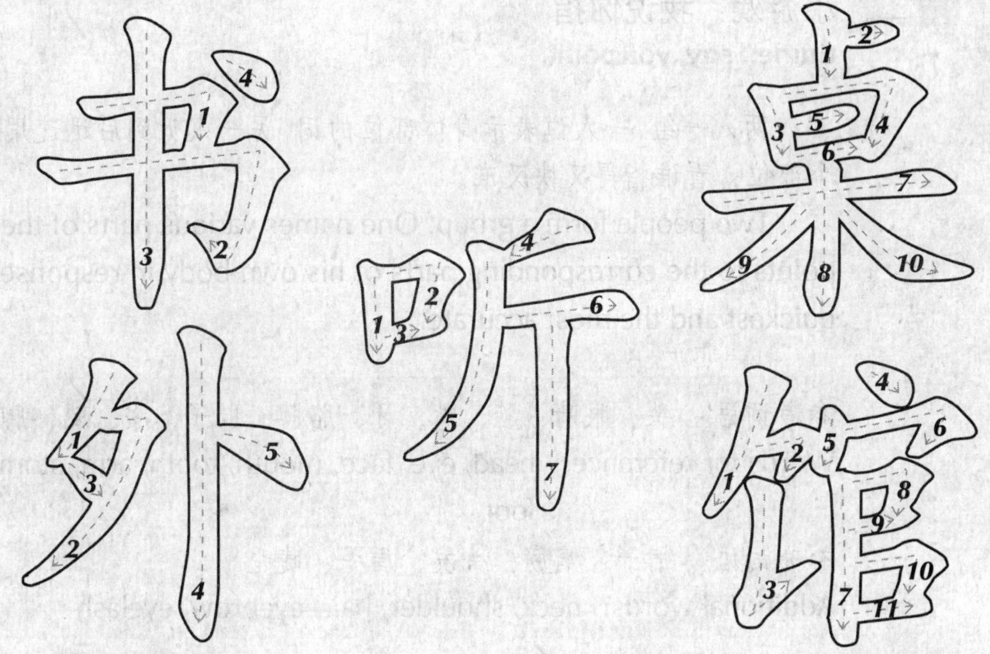

十七、实践活动：用汉语制作一个你家、学校、公司附近的街道地图。并向老师和同学解释你的地图

Practice: Draw a street map of your home, school and company. Explain your map to your teacher and classmates.

Unit 9 你怎么了？

课堂活动

第1部分

一、学习表示身体主要部位的词语

Learn the expressions concerning the main parts of the body.

1. 跟老师用汉语说出身体的主要部位。Follow the teacher to identify the main parts of the body in Chinese.

2. 找一名同学当模特，其他同学用汉语说出他/她身体的主要部位。Find a classmate to serve as a model.The others may identify the main parts of the body in Chinese.

二、小游戏：我说你指

Game: I say, you point.

两人一组，一人说表示身体部位的词，另一人听到后迅速用手指着自己的那个部位，看谁指得又快又准。

Two people form a group. One names various parts of the body; the other points to the corresponding parts of his own body in response. See who is the quickest and the most accurate.

参考词语：头、眼睛、脸、嘴、牙、胳膊、肚子、手、腿、脚
Words for reference: head, eye, face, mouth, tooth, arm, stomach,hand, leg, foot

补充词语：脖子、肩膀、头发、眉毛、睫毛
Additional words: neck, shoulder, hair, eyebrow, eyelash

三、小游戏：我演你猜

Game: I play, you guess.

全班同学分为两组。A组同学每人抽取一个词语卡片，把词语的意思表演出

来，B组同学猜测并用汉语说出来。

The whole class is divided into two groups. Everyone in group A takes out a card with a word on it and conducts a performance based on the meaning of the word, while group B tries to guess what the word is in Chinese.

参考词语：头疼、发烧、牙疼、咳嗽、腿疼、胃疼/肚子疼、嗓子疼
Words for reference: have a headache, have a fever, have a toothache/cough, have pains in the leg, have a stomachache/sore throat

四、看图完成对话
Look at the pictures and complete the dialogues.

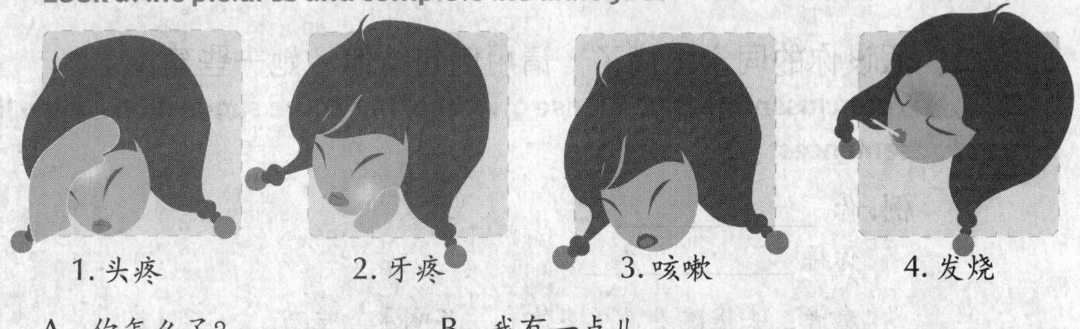

1. 头疼　2. 牙疼　3. 咳嗽　4. 发烧

A：你怎么了？　B：我有一点儿 ______________。

五、角色扮演
Role-Play

两人一组，一人演医生，一人演病人，模仿课文表演看病情节，看哪一组表演得最好。Two people form a group, one playing the doctor, the other the patient. Imitate the lesson to reenact the visit to the doctor. See which group performs best.

第2部分

一、看图完成句子
Look at the pictures and complete the sentences.

1. 去银行

2. 去大使馆

3. 骑自行车

我今天 ______________ 不能 ______________ 了。

二、假设你的同学生病了，请用例句给他／她一些建议
Your classmate is ill. Please give him/her some suggestions using the sample sentences.

例： 你 ______________ 吧。

你得 ______________。

参考：去医院看看、多休息、多喝水、吃药

三、两人一组，完成对话
Work in pairs and complete the dialogue.

A：我今天不能 ______________ 了。

B：______________？

A：我有点儿 ______________。

B：你得 ______________。

A：我去了，医生说我得多休息。

B：你 ________ 吧。我告诉 ______________。

四、四人一组，每人抽取一个句子，然后组成一个对话
Form a group of four people, and each of them should select a sentence then make a dialogue together.

A. 你怎么了？

B. 你休息吧。我和姐姐一起去。

C. 我有点儿不舒服。

D. 我今天不能去长城了。

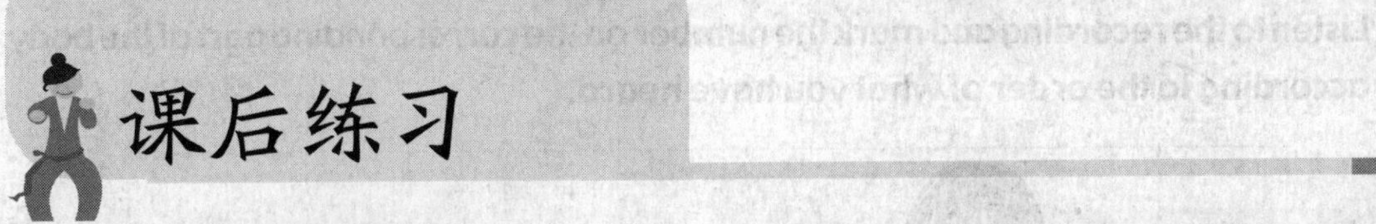

课后练习

一、听录音，填写声母或韵母

Listen to the recording and fill in the initial or the final sound of a syllable.

__ào
__ào
__ǎn
__ǎn

t__
t__
sh__
sh__

二、听录音，标出声调

Listen to the recording and mark the tones.

yi xiu bing shui ke fa xi yao tou gao

三、听录音，选出你听到的音节

Listen to the recording and select the syllables you have heard.

shuō	( )	duō	( )
gào	( )	mào	( )
gǎn	( )	bǎn	( )
nǐ	( )	xǐ	( )
shuǐ	( )	shuí	( )
gěi	( )	děi	( )
xǐhuan	( )	yīyuàn	( )
késou	( )	péngyou	( )
chīyào	( )	zhīdào	( )

四、听录音，按听到的顺序在相应的身体部位标上序号

Listen to the recording and mark the number on the corresponding part of the body according to the order of what you have heard.

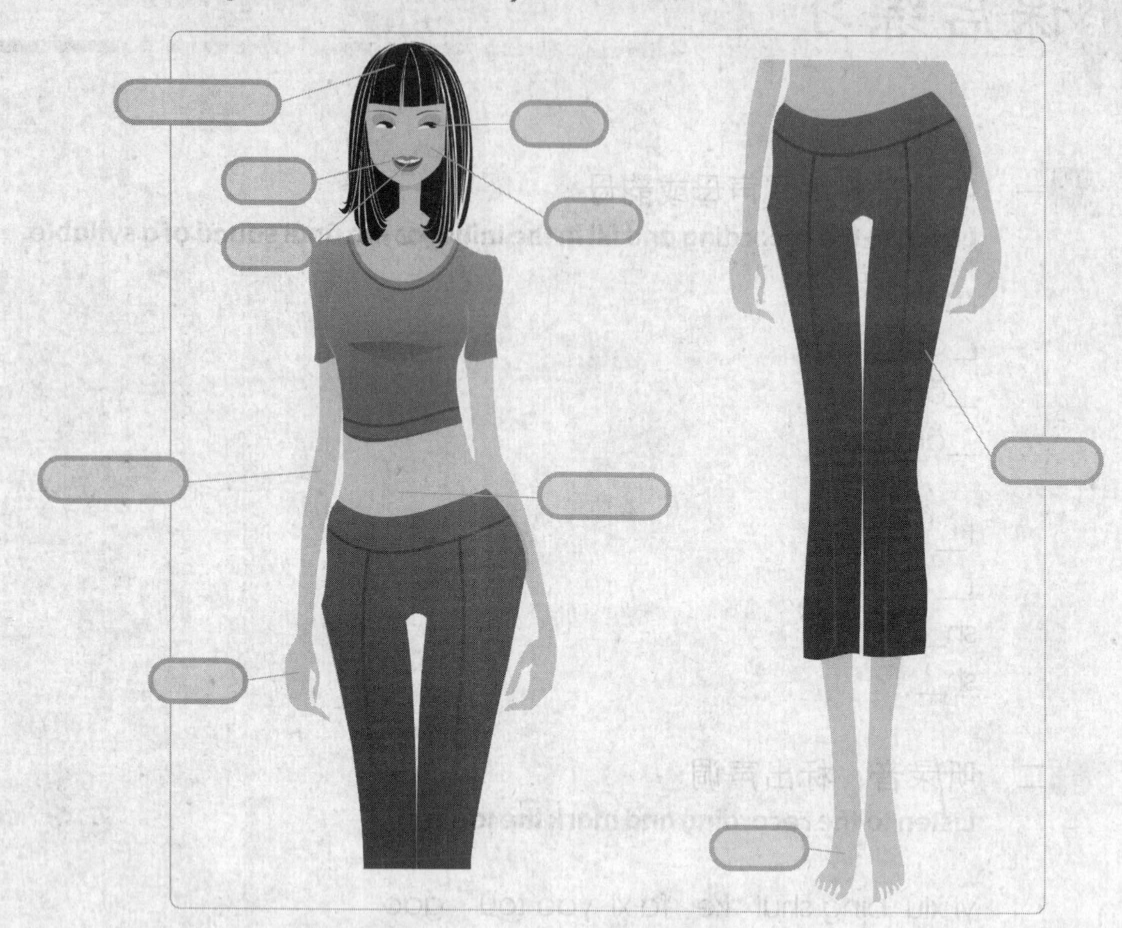

五、听录音，选出你听到的句子

Listen to the recording and select the sentence you've heard.

1	我感冒了。		我发烧了。	
2	我有一点儿头疼。		我有一点儿牙疼。	
3	你得去医院看病。		你得找医生看看。	
4	我今天不能上班了。		我今天不能上课了。	

六、听录音，选择合适的应答语

Listen to the recording and select your suitable replies.

1. （　） A. 我头疼。 B. 你感冒了。
2. （　） A. 不疼。 B. 咳嗽。
3. （　） A. 我不喝。 B. 不喜欢。

七、听录音，选择正确答案
Listen to the recording and select the right answers.

1. 马丁怎么了？
   A. 累了。 B. 病了。

2. 张华中午去哪儿？
   A. 药店。 B. 医院。

八、根据拼音写出两个同音字
Write out two homophones according to the *pinyin*.

shāo (　　) (　　)
yī (　　) (　　)
yào (　　) (　　)

九、用"吃"和"喝"填空
Fill in the blanks with the word "eat" and "drink".

1. (　　) 水
2. (　　) 饭
3. (　　) 菜
4. (　　) 酒
5. (　　) 茶
6. (　　) 汤

十、选词填空
Fill in the blanks with the chosen words.

吃　一点儿　看　有点儿
1. 你去医院（　　　　　）病吧。
2. 我不喜欢（　　　　　）药。
3. 我（　　　　　）不舒服。
4. 你喝（　　　　　）酒吧。

十一、连词成句
Make sentences by linking the words.

1. 有 不 一点儿 我 舒服

________________________________。

2. 得 医院 你 病 看 去

________________________。

3. 上课 能 了 不 去 我

________________________。

十二、阅读并回答问题
Read and answer the questions.

请假条

张老师：

您好！

我感冒了，有点儿头疼，今天不能去上课了。向您请一天假。

学生：宋丽丽

10月18日

1. 谁不能去上课？她怎么了？

________________________。

2. 她的老师姓什么？

________________________。

3. 她请几天假？

________________________。

十三、找出下列每组汉字中相同的部件
Identify the common components within each of the following groups of Chinese characters.

例：昨 明 晚 （日）

1. 你 休 什 （ ）
2. 感 息 您 （ ）
3. 疼 病 痛 （ ）
4. 桥 椅 板 （ ）

十四、用下列部件组合成你学过的汉字

Combine the following components to form the Chinese characters you have learnt.

例如： 扌+丁→打

亻 木 自 心 咸 一 巨 疒 冬 丙

① ____ ② ____ ③ ____ ④ ____ ⑤ ____ ⑥ ____ ⑦ ____

十五、按笔顺将下列汉字书写五遍

Write the following Chinese characters five times each, following the proper stroke order.

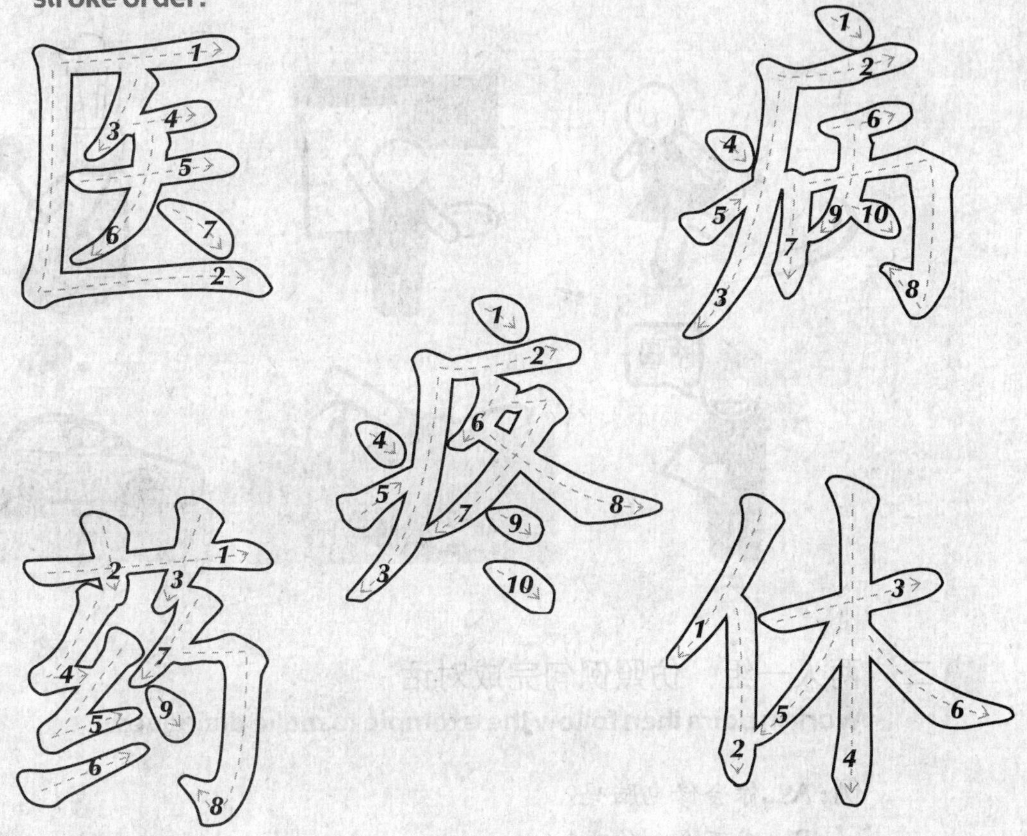

十六、实践活动：用汉语写一个请假条

Practice: Write a sample request for leave in Chinese.

Unit 10 你会修电脑吗?

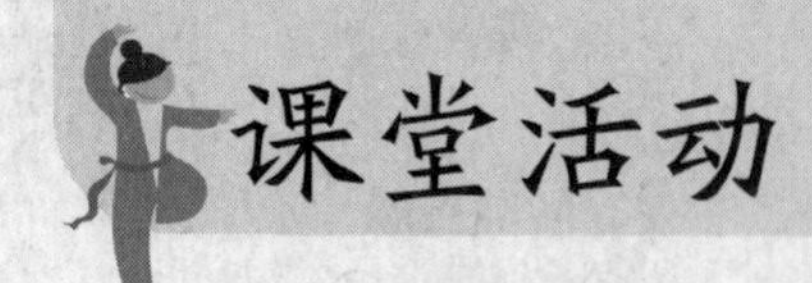

课堂活动

第 1 部分

一、看图说出下列活动
Look at the picture and point out the following activities.

二、两人一组，仿照例句完成对话
Work in pairs then follow the example to make dialogues.

例：A：你会修电脑吗？
B：我不会。你呢？
A：我也不会。

我/同学

修电脑　骑自行车　修冰箱

说法语　画画　上网

三、四人一组，每人抽取一个句子，然后组成一个对话
Form a group of four people. Each student draws a sentence and the group then make a dialogue.

A. 画得不太好。

B. 会一点儿。

C. 画得怎么样？

D. 你会画画吗？

四、两人一组，看图完成对话
Work in pairs and look at the pictures and complete the dialogues.

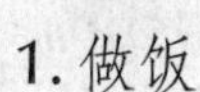

1. 做饭　　2. 开车　　3. 游泳　　4. 滑冰

A：你会＿＿＿＿＿＿吗？

B：我会。/ 我会一点儿。

A：＿＿得怎么样？

B：＿＿＿＿＿＿。

第2部分

一、说说你最喜欢做的和最不喜欢做的活动
Discuss the activities that you like and dislike most.

最喜欢	最不喜欢

二、两人一组，完成下表，然后仿照例子说一段话

Work in pairs.Complete the following form and follow the example to give an oral presentation.

例：

我常常走路，有时候骑自行车。我从不开车。

	从　不	有时候	常　常
开　车			
骑自行车			
做　饭			
说汉语			
画　画			
游　泳			
滑　冰			
上　网			
去健身房			
打网球			
看电视			

三、仿照例句采访班里3个同学，完成表格

Follow the example to interview three of your classmates and complete the form.

例： 放学以后你常常做什么？一星期几次？

	姓　名	活　动	次　数
1			
2			
3			

四、五人一组，每人抽取一个句子，然后组成一个对话

Form a group of five people. Each of them should selects a sentence and then make a dialogue together.

A. 放学以后你常常做什么？

B. 一星期几次？

C. 我有时候去健身房。

D. 在家做作业。有时候上网。你呢？

E. 三次。

五、看图完成句子

Look at the picture and complete the sentence.

1. 买东西　2. 爬山　3. 游泳　4. 去健身房　5. 吃饭

例：我们一起 ________________ 吧。

六、两人一组，选择下面的问题进行会话，至少用上三个问题

Work in pairs, then choose at least three of the following questions to make a dialogue.

1. ______ 以后你常常做什么？
2. 你呢？
3. 一星期几次？
4. 周末你常常做什么？
5. 这周末你有空吗？
6. 我们一起 ______，好吗？

课后练习

一、听录音，填写声母或韵母

Listen to the recording and fill in the initial or the final sound of a syllable.

__āng

__áng

__iū

__iú

h__

h__

k__

k__

二、听录音，标出声调

Listen to the recording and mark the tones.

yi du nao zhou ci mo qi jian shen wang

三、听录音，选出你听到的音节

Listen to the recording and select the syllables you have heard.

xiū	(　　)	xīn	(　　)
kǒng	(　　)	gǒng	(　　)
cháng	(　　)	fáng	(　　)
nǎo	(　　)	lǎo	(　　)
huì	(　　)	guì	(　　)
huà	(　　)	huá	(　　)
hàn	(　　)	diàn	(　　)
huài	(　　)	kuài	(　　)

四、听录音，按听到的顺序为下图标上序号

Listen to the recording and mark the numbers for the following pictures according to the order of what you have heard.

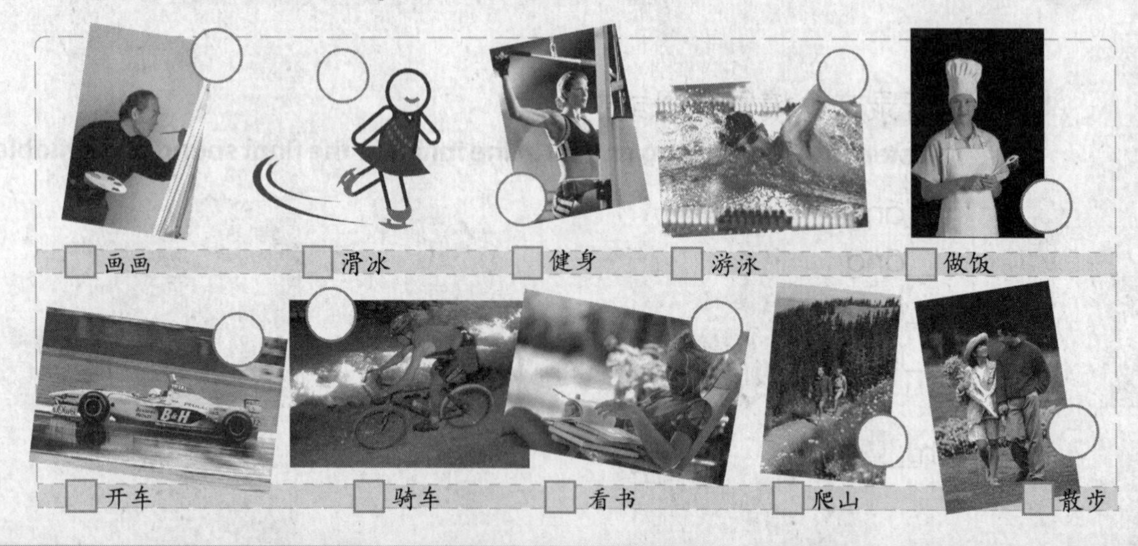

五、听录音，填空

Listen to the recording and fill in the blanks.

1. 下班以后我__________去游泳。
2. __________我常常去买东西。
3. __________以后我总是去公园散步。
4. 周末我__________去爬山。

六、听录音，判断正误

Listen to the recording and judge what you have heard is right or wrong.

1. 他今天要去游泳。 ( )
2. 他一星期游两次泳。( )
3. 他常常去健身房。 ( )
4. 他很喜欢打网球。 ( )
5. 他网球打得很好。 ( )

七、看汉字，写拼音

Look at the Chinese characters and write down the *pinyin* (the Chinese Phonetic Alphabet) for them.

修　　电脑　　可能　　周末　　下班　　会

八、给下列汉字组词

Use the following Chinese characters to form a word.

电:_____ _____　　病:_____ _____

上:_____ _____　　房:_____ _____

九、用括号里的词改写句子

Rewrite the sentences using the words in the brackets.

他会说汉语。

1. ______________________________ (会不会)
2. ______________________________ (吗)
3. ______________________________ (不会)

十、连词成句
Make sentences by linking the words.

1. 一点儿　我　会

______________________________。

2. 一起　我们　吧　健身房　去

______________________________。

3. 你　车　修　听说　会

______________________________。

4. 很　打　他　好　得

______________________________。

十一、回答问题
Answer the questions.

1. 你会修电脑吗？

____

2. 你会画画吗？

____

3. 你会游泳吗？

____

4. 放学以后你常常做什么？

____

5. 周末你常常做什么？

____

十二、阅读并回答问题
Read and answer the questions.

王先生的业余生活

	星期一	星期二	星期三	星期四	星期五	星期六	星期日
上午						在家休息 买东西(有时候)	
下午	游泳	打网球	游泳	游泳			
晚上	散步	散步	散步	散步	散步	看书	看电视

1. 完成短文。Complete the passage.

王先生下班以后常常去 ______________，一周去 ______ 次，有时候也去 ______________。晚上常常去 ______________。周末常常 ____________，有时候去 ____________。星期六晚上常常 ____________，星期日晚上 ____________。

2. 模仿上文，写一段话介绍你的业余生活。Imitate the passage above and write a passage of your own to introduce your spare time.

十三、按笔画数由少到多排列汉字

Arrange the Chinese characters in the order of ascending number of strokes.

会 修 脑 坏 网 毒 常 球 空

十四、写出有下列部首的汉字

Write down the Chinese characters that consist of the following parts.

1. 扌：____ ____
2. 月：____ ____
3. 彳：____ ____

十五、按笔顺将下列汉字书写五遍

Write the following Chinese characters five times each, following the proper stroke order.

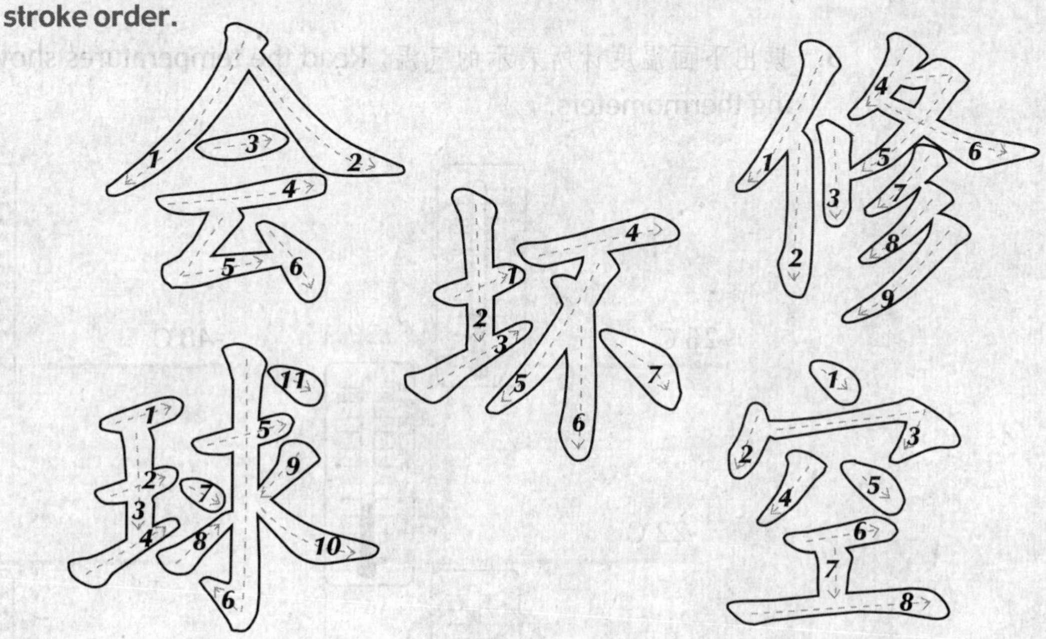

十六、实践活动：找一个中国朋友，聊聊他／她的业余生活并记录下来

Practice: Find a Chinese friend to discuss his/her spare time and take notes.

Unit 11 太冷了！

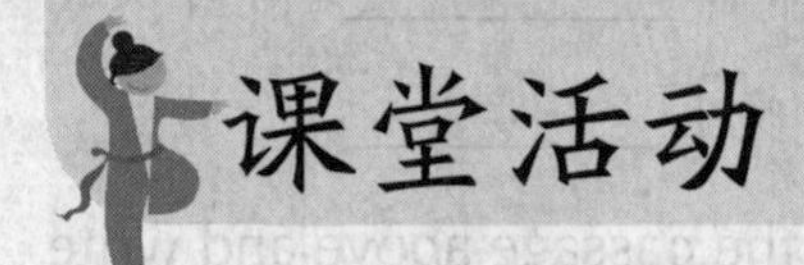

第1部分

一、复习数字，学习气温表达法

Review the numbers and learn the expressions about temperatures.

1. 请用汉语说出今天当地的气温。In Chinese, give the local temperature today.

   请用母语说出你觉得最舒服的气温，并跟老师用汉语说出来。(选做题)Please speak in your native language, identify the temperature that makes you feel the most comfortable and then communicate the same to the teacher in Chinese. (optional)

2. 跟老师用汉语说出下面数字表示的温度。In Chinese, read out the following temperatures to the teacher.

   -21℃　-10℃　-3℃　8℃　17℃　22℃　35℃　42℃

3. 读出下面温度计所表示的气温。Read the temperatures shown in the following thermometers.

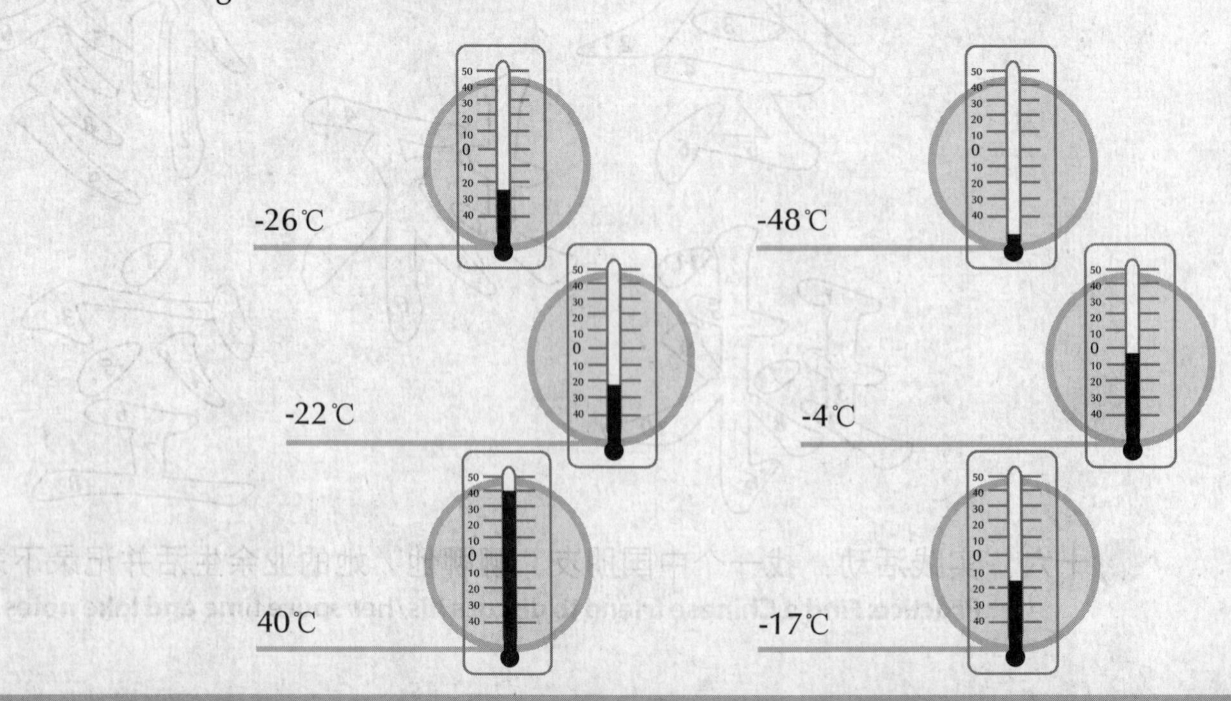

二、先用汉语说出下列气温，然后用线把气温与相对应的感觉连起来。每个气温只能选一个词

In Chinese, read out the temperature, then link the temperature with the corresponding feeling. Only one word can be chosen for each temperature.

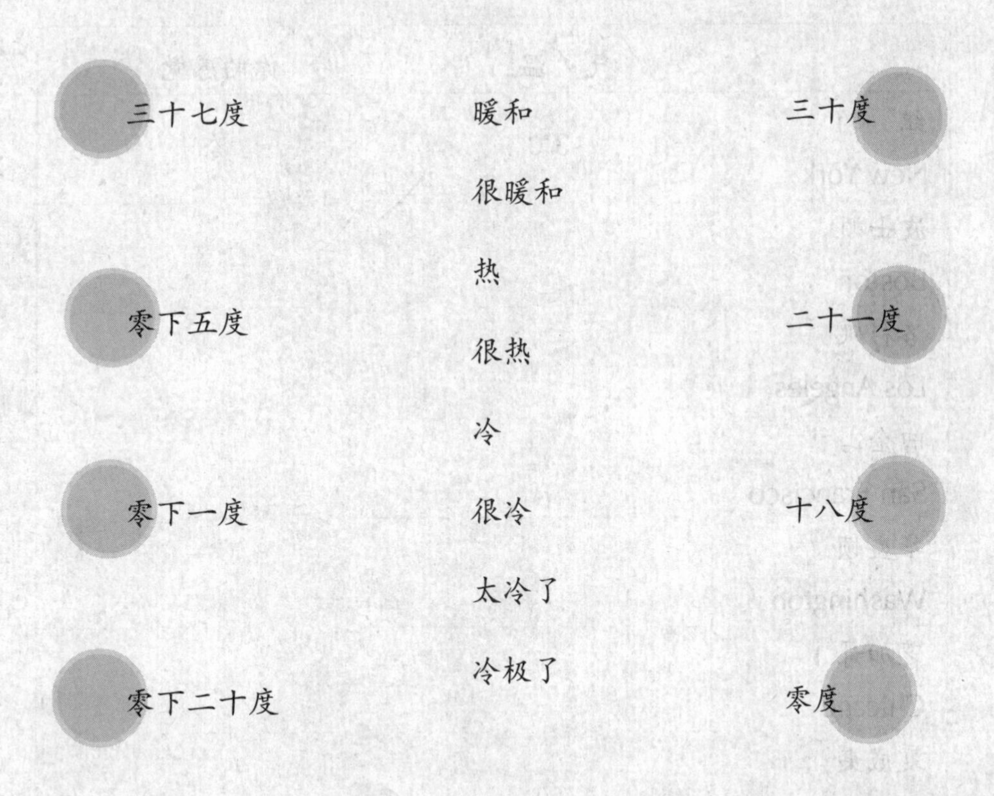

三、仿照例句，完成句子

Follow the example to complete the following sentences.

1. **例：**那儿的天气　太　冷　了。

哈尔滨的冰灯________________。
北京的长城________________。
你的T恤________________。

2. **例：**哈尔滨　比　北京　冷　多了。

春天______冬天　暖和______。
夏天______秋天　热______。
哥哥______弟弟　胖______。

四、两人一组，仿照例句讨论某个城市的天气和气温，完成表格

Work in pairs. Follow the example to discuss the weather and temperature of a

sh__
x__
x__

二、听录音，标出声调
Listen to the recording and mark the tones.

a yi yun sao huar wai xi ling

三、听录音，选出你听到的音节
Listen to the recording and select the syllables you have heard.

qiǎn	( )	qián	( )
cā	( )	chā	( )
sǎn	( )	wǎn	( )
fàn	( )	kàn	( )
sháo	( )	shāo	( )
bǎ	( )	dǎ	( )
shēn	( )	shēng	( )
yíxiàr	( )	yīdiǎnr	( )

四、听录音，按听到的顺序为下图标上序号
Listen to the recording and mark the numbers for the following pictures according to the order of what you have heard.

1.

2.

certain city, and complete the form.

例：A：纽约的气温是多少度？
B：零下三度。
A：那儿的天气太冷了。

	气　温	你的感觉
纽　约 New York	-3℃	冷
波士顿 Boston		
洛杉矶 Los Angeles		
旧金山 San Francisco		
华盛顿 Washington		
芝加哥 Chicago		
夏威夷 Hawaii		
亚特兰大 Atlanta		

五、用给定的情景替换练习下面的对话

Practise the following dialogues according to the given situation.

（1）北京　上海　　（2）天津　广州　　（3）西安　香港

A：北京的天气怎么样？那儿的气温是多少度？

B：下雪，零下8度。上海呢？

A：晴，12度。

B：北京的天气太冷了，比上海冷多了。

A：对，上海的天气比北京暖和多了。

一、复习表示天气的名词，学习天气表达法

Review the nouns that indicate the weather, learn the expressions about the weather.

1. 请用汉语说出你所知道的表示天气的名词。Use Chinese, to say the the nouns that indicate the weather in a loud voice.

2. 请用汉语说出你最喜欢的一种天气。Use Chinese to describe the kind of weather that you like or dislike most.

3. 根据实际情况回答问题。Answer the questions according to the practical situation.

问	答
(1) 今天是什么天气？	今天_________。
(2) 昨天是什么天气？	昨天_________。
(3) 前天是什么天气？	前天_________。

4. 跟老师用汉语说出下列图示的天气。Use Chinese to describe to the teacher the weather shown in the following pictures.

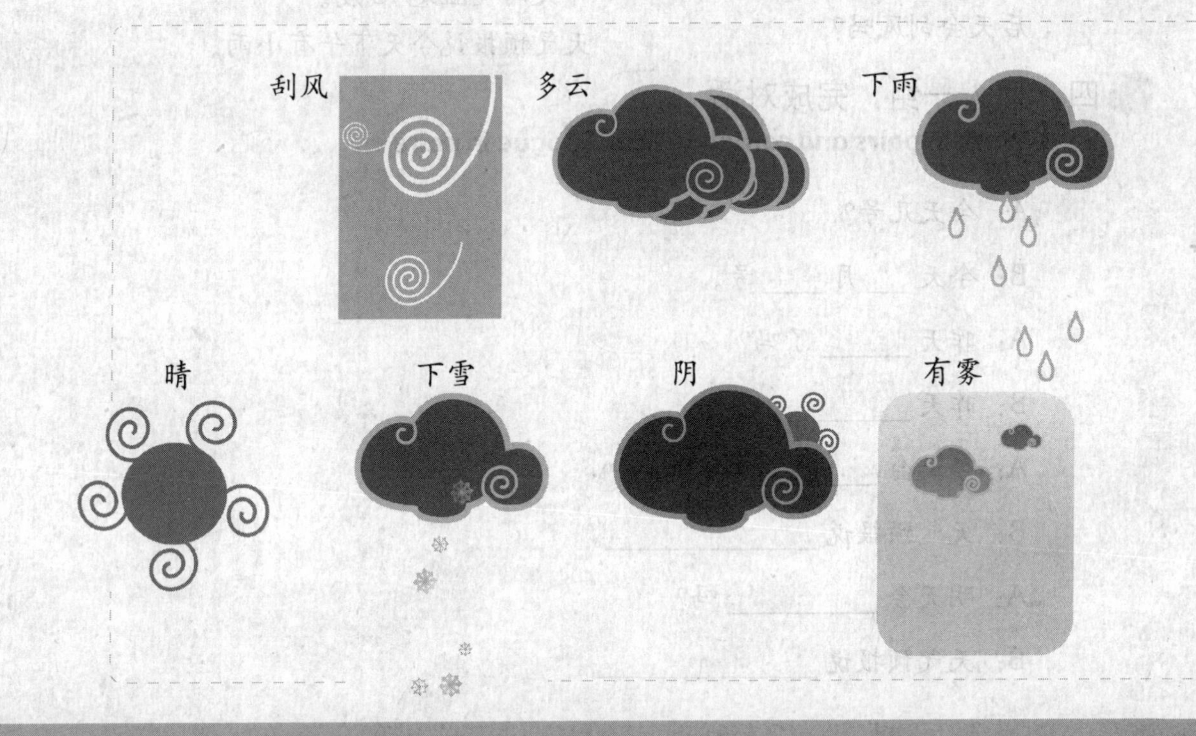

二、朗读下面的句子
Read aloud the following sentences.

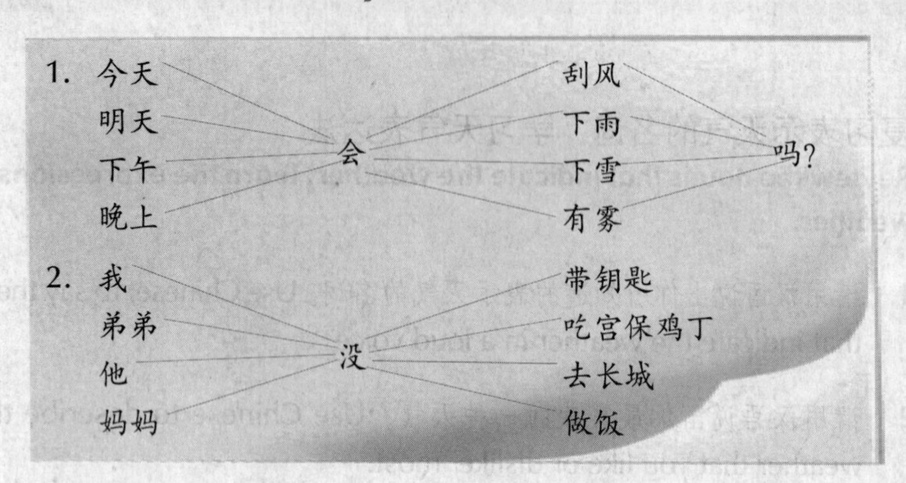

三、抽签问答。请抽到问题的同学按顺序提问，抽到相应答案的同学回答
Ask questions and give answers by drawing lots. Those who draw questions should ask them in turn; those who draw answers should give the corresponding replies.

昨天是什么天气？
昨天的气温是多少度？
今天上午下雨了吗？
今天下午会下雨吗？
明天是什么天气？
明天的气温是多少度？
后天会刮风吗？

天气预报说后天有大风。
明天的气温是17度。
明天有雾。
昨天多云。
今天上午没下雨。
昨天的气温是19度。
天气预报说今天下午有小雨。

四、两人一组，完成对话
Work in pairs and complete the dialogue in pairs.

A：今天几号？

B：今天____月____号。

A：昨天______了吗？

B：昨天__________。

A：今天会________吗？

B：天气预报说______________。

A：明天会__________吗？

B：天气预报说______________。

五、两人一组，根据给出的场景完成对话
Work in pairs. Complete the dialogues according to the given situations.

1. （在去飞机场的路上）

A：昨天看了天气预报吗？今天________________？

B：看了，____________________________。

A：太好了，飞机不会晚点了。

2. （去爬山前）

A：明天去爬山吗？

B：可是天气预报说________________________，温度______________。

A：没关系，________________________。

B：好吧，我和你一起去爬山吧。

A：________________________。

六、两人一组，选择下面的句型进行会话，至少用上三个句型
Choose the following sentence patterns to make up a dialogue in pairs, using at least three of them.

……极了。（漂亮、好看、暖和、聪明、潮湿、干燥、便宜、舒服）
那儿的天气很……（冷、热、暖和）
那儿的天气太……了。（冷、热）
那儿的气温是多少度？
……比……冷/热/暖和。
……比……冷/热/暖和多了。
今天/明天/后天/上午/下午会……吗？（刮风、下雨、下雪、有雾）
我/你/他没……

例：A：北京的天气怎么样？

B：北京干燥极了，天气很冷。

A：现在那儿的气温是多少度？

B：零下十度。

A：北京的天气比旧金山冷多了。

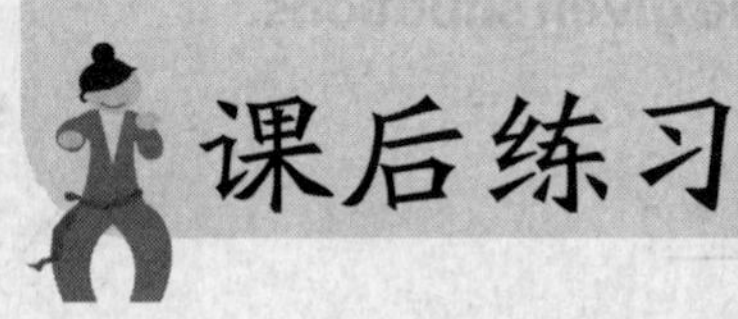

课后练习

一、听录音，填写声母或韵母

Listen to the recording and fill in the initial or the final sound of a syllable.

__uǎng
__uāng
__uǎng
__uǎn

r__
r__
r__

二、听录音，标出声调

Listen to the recording and mark the tones.

chu　wan　zui　lü　teng

三、听录音，选出你听到的音节

Listen to the recording and check(✓) the syllables you have heard.

rì　(　)　　lì　(　)
zhé　(　)　　zé　(　)
qū　(　)　　chū　(　)
tǎo　(　)　　dǎo　(　)
yīng　(　)　　yīn　(　)
sū　(　)　　xū　(　)

四、听录音，按听到的顺序在相应的图下面写上序号

Listen to the recording and write down the sequence numbers below the corre-

sponding pictures according to the order of what you have heard.

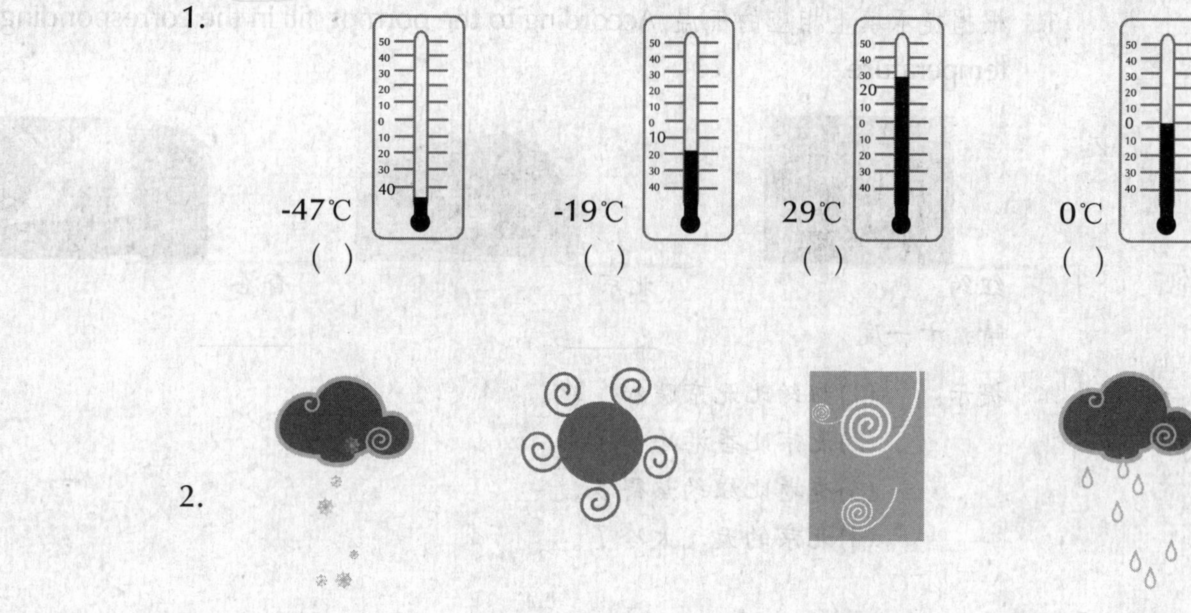

1. -47℃ ( ) -19℃ ( ) 29℃ ( ) 0℃ ( )

2. -12℃ ( ) 38℃ ( ) 8℃ ( ) 12℃ ( )

五、听录音，选择正确答案

Listen to the recording and choose the right answers.

1. A. -3℃。 B. -13℃。
2. A. 纽约比旧金山暖和得多。 B. 纽约比旧金山冷多了。
3. A. 今天会下雨。 B. 今天没下雨。

六、看汉字，写拼音

Look at the Chinese characters and write down the *pinyin* (the Chinese Phonetic Alphabet) for them.

暖和 下雪 旅行 零下

七、看拼音，用汉字写出句子

Look at the *pinyin* and write down the sentence using Chinese characters.

1. Nǎr de qìwēn shì duōshǎo dù?

2. Tiānqì yùbào shuō jīntiān yǒu dàyǔ.

八、根据提示填空

Fill in the blanks with the corresponding weather and temperature as prompted.

1. 根据提示填上相应的气温。According to the pormpt, fill in the corresponding temperature.

纽约	北京	香港
晴，十一度	______	______

提示：(1)纽约比北京暖和。
(2)北京比香港冷多了。
(3)香港比纽约热得多。
(4)北京的天气太冷了。

2. 先填上相应的时间词，再根据提示填上相应的温度。First, fill in the corresponding time words, and then fill in the corresponding temperature.

星期三 7号	星期四 8号	星期六 10号
	阴，10℃	
______	今天	______

提示：(1)今天比昨天冷。
(2)昨天天气比今天暖和。
(3)天气预报说后天有小雪。
(4)后天下雪，天气比今天冷多了。

九、连词成句

Rearrange the words to make a sentence.

1. 冬天 春天 冷 比 多了

______________。

2. 说 今天 会 天气预报 下雨

______________。

3. 没 昨天 我 游泳 去 早上

______________。

十、完成下面的短文
Complete the following short passage.

上个星期我去北京旅行。北京的故宫______，可是北京的天气__________。那儿的气温是_________，比纽约__________。

这个星期我在纽约学习，昨天天气预报说______，可是我________雨伞，老师________我一把。

十一、阅读并回答问题
Read and answer the questions.

1. 马丁的日记。The diary of Martin.

2006年6月19日　星期一　大雨　30℃

昨天天气预报说今天没有雨，可是今天上午下大雨了。我没带伞，丽丽给了我一把伞。昨天比今天热，今天比昨天舒服，可是我不能去爬山了。

丽丽说，北京的夏天很热，常常下雨，潮湿极了。我不喜欢北京夏天的天气，可是我喜欢北京。

(1) 昨天的天气预报说了什么？

______________________________________。

(2) 马丁淋了雨吗？

______________________________________。

(3) 马丁原计划今天做什么事？

______________________________________。

2. 王先生本周的运动日程表。Mr. Wang's sports schedule this week.

时间	计划	天气
星期一	骑自行车	晴，6℃
星期二	去体育馆滑冰	多云，5℃
星期三	去公园散步	小雨，3℃
星期四	网球	阴，3℃
星期五	去游泳馆游泳	有风，1℃
星期六	爬山	下雪，-5℃
星期天	去健身房健身	有风，-6℃

(1) 王先生计划星期几去公园散步？能去吗？

____

(2) 王先生计划星期几去游泳？能去吗？

____

(3) 这个星期哪一天天气最好？

____

(4) 这个星期哪一天天气最差？这一天王先生计划做什么？

____

(5) 这个星期王先生能做几项运动？

____

十二、数一数下列汉字的笔画，把笔画数写在下面

Count the strokes of the following Chinese characters and write the numbers of stroke below.

气　温　冷　雨　晴　零

_____ _____ _____ _____ _____ _____

十三、按笔顺将下列汉字书写五遍

Write the following Chinese characters five times each, following the proper stroke order.

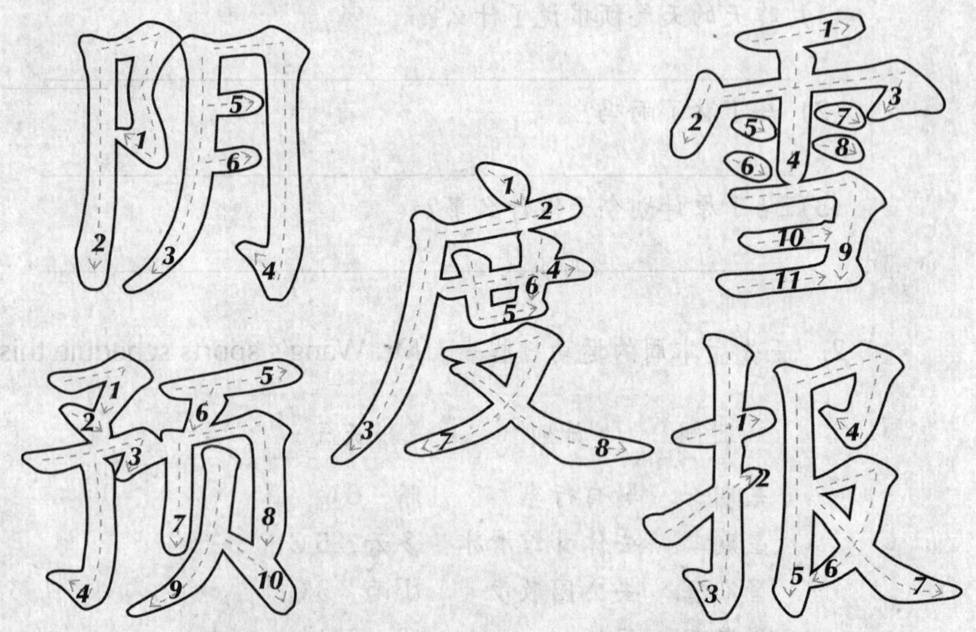

十四、实践活动：用汉语为你所在城市做下一周的天气预报

Practice: Use Chinese to forecast the weather for the city in which you are currently located.

Unit 12 请把桌子擦一下儿?

课堂活动

第1部分

一、看图说词语

Look at the pictures and say the words out loud.

客厅 卧室 厨房 书房 卫生间

门 窗户 窗帘 床 沙发

椅子 茶几 桌子 书柜 衣柜

二、请说说教室里的摆设

Please describe the furnishings of the classroom.

三、请说说学过的表示家具的词语

Please talk about the words you have learnt that indicate furniture.

四、用所给词语完成句子
Complete the sentence using the given words.

擦 桌子　　洗 衣服　　熨 衣服　　打扫 卫生间

例：请把 ________ ________ 一下儿。

五、两人一组，读对话，学会答应别人要求的词句
Read the dialogue in pairs and learn the words and sentences that reply to your partner's request.

1. A：小姐，别放味精。
   B：好。
2. A：我是她的朋友张华，请她给我回电话。
   B：行。
3. A：请你把厨房收拾一下儿。
   B：没问题。

六、四人一组，每人抽取一个句子，然后组成一个对话
Form a group of four people. Each of them draws a sentence,and then creates a dialogue together.

A. 要。另外，把这些碗洗一下儿。

B. 没问题。

C. 好。这张桌子要收拾吗？

D. 阿姨，请把卫生间打扫一下儿。

第2部分

一、请说出学过的表示餐具的词语
Please pronounce the words you have learnt that indicate tableware.

二、看图完成句子
Look at the pictures and complete the sentences.

例： 请把花插到花瓶里。

1. 水果、桌子
2. 肉、冰箱

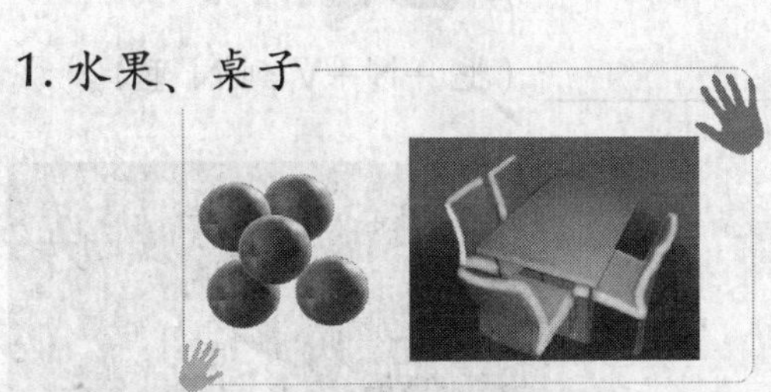

3. 花瓶、窗台
4. 蔬菜、厨房

三、采访3个同学，回答问题
Interview three of your classmates and answer the question.

问题： 今天晚上你做什么？

	姓　名	活　动
1		
2		
3		

例： 今天晚上李华和朋友一起吃饭。

四、两人一组，看图完成对话
Work in pairs,and look at the pictures and complete the dialogues.

阿姨： 你好！今天要做什么？

A： ________________________ （请把＋N＋V一下儿）。

阿姨： 行。

A：＿＿＿＿＿＿＿＿＿＿＿＿＿＿＿＿（把＋N＋V 到 N 里）。

阿姨：好。

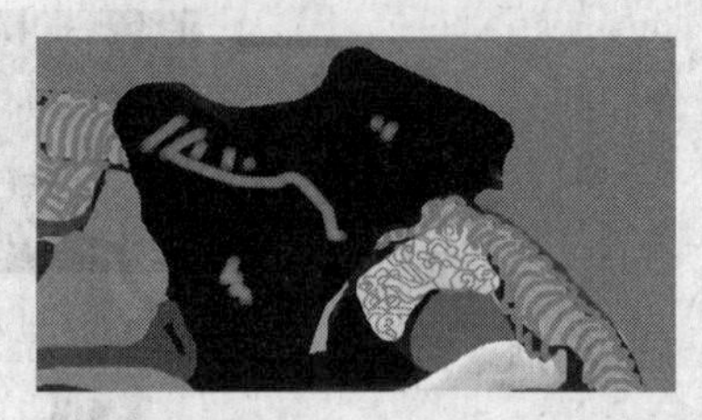

A：＿＿＿＿＿＿＿＿＿＿＿＿＿＿＿＿（另外，把＋N＋V 一下儿。）

阿姨：没问题。

五、角色扮演
Role-Play

两人一组，一人演阿姨，一人演主人，模仿课文表演安排家务的情节，看哪一组表演得最好。Two persons form a group, one playing the nanny, the other the host. Imitate the lesson to reenact the arrangement of the housework. See which group performs best.

课后练习

一、听录音，填写声母或韵母
Listen to the recording and fill in the initial or the final sound of a syllable.

__iān

__iǎn

__ā

__ā

sh__

3.

(　) (　) (　) (　) (　)

五、听录音，选出你听到的句子

Listen to the recording and choose the sentences you have heard.

1. 今天晚上我去商店。　今天晚上我去饭店。
2. 那些衣服要洗吗？　这些衣服要洗吗？
3. 请把水果洗一下。　请把衣服洗一下。
4. 把这些筷子放到桌子上。　把这些勺子放到桌子上。

六、听录音，选择合适的应答语

Listen to the recording and choose your suitable replies.

1. (　) A. 好 B. 要
2. (　) A. 是 B. 要
3. (　) A. 没问题 B. 对
4. (　) A. 对 B. 在

七、看汉字，写拼音

Look at the Chinese characters and write down the *pinyin* (the Chinese Phonetic Alphabet) for them.

深　浅　洗　打扫　水果　晚　蔬菜　饭

八、根据拼音写出两个同音字

Write out two homophones according to the *pinyin*.

shū (　) (　)
kuài (　) (　)
wǎn (　) (　)

九、选出一个不同类的词

Pick out the word that does not belong to the same category.

1. 卧室　客厅　沙发　书房　(　　)

2. 鱼　肉　饭　书　(　　)
3. 洗　熨　把　擦　插　(　　)
4. 床　茶几　沙发　厨房　桌子　(　　)

十、选词填空
Fill in the blanks with the chosen words.

擦　放　插　熨
把这些衣服（　）一下。
把这张桌子（　）一下。
把这些花儿（　）到花瓶里。
把花瓶（　）到窗台上。

十一、用“把”完成句子
Complete the sentences using the word “把”.

例：苹果　冰箱
　　把苹果放到冰箱里。

1. 碗　　厨房
________________。

2. 书　　桌子
________________。

3. 毛衣　　衣柜
________________。

4. 草莓　　碗
________________。

十二、阅读并回答问题
Read and answer the questions.

阿姨：

今天晚上我要请朋友来家里吃饭，请你晚点儿走。我去商店买东西了。请你先把厨房收拾一下儿，把这些衣服洗一下儿，把卫生间也打扫一下儿。另外，把窗台上的花放到桌子上。我回来以后，我们一起做饭。

宋丽丽
11月5日

1. 宋丽丽晚上要做什么？

______________________________。

2. 宋丽丽去哪儿了？

______________________________。

3. 宋丽丽让阿姨先做什么？

______________________________。

十三、按笔画数由少到多排列汉字

Arrange the Chinese characters in the order of ascending number of strokes.

把　擦　衣　洗　深　浅　碗　瓶

____ ____ ____ ____ ____ ____ ____ ____

十四、用下面的部件组合成你学过的汉字

Combine the following parts to form the Chinese characters you have learnt.

例： 扌＋丁→打

扌　巴　氵　冫　先　令　并　瓦　石　宛　察　父

①____ ②____ ③____ ④____ ⑤____ ⑥____ ⑦____

十五、按笔顺将下列汉字书写五遍

Write the following Chinese characters five times each, following the proper stroke order.

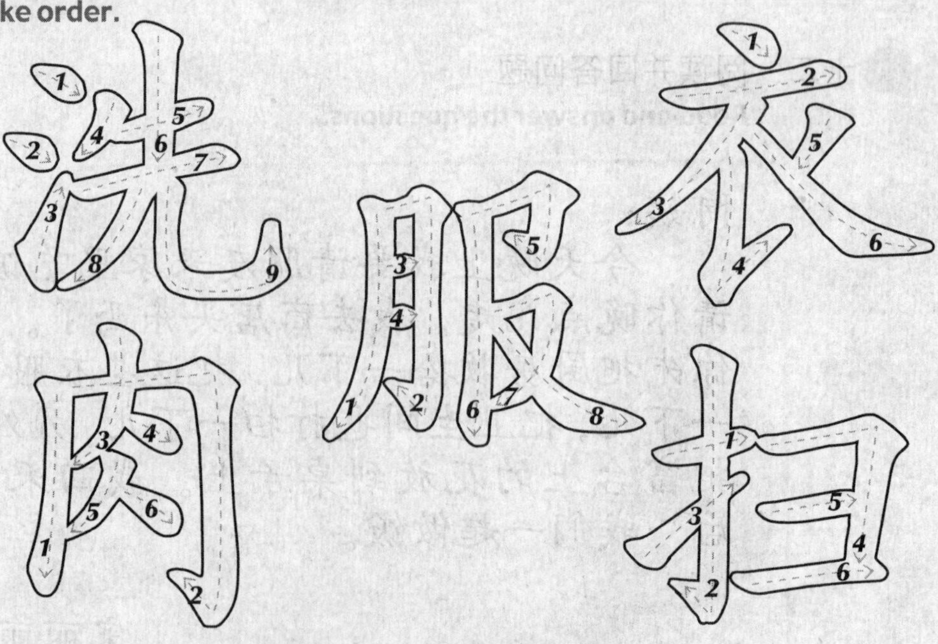

十六、实践活动：用汉语给阿姨安排家务

Practice: In Chinese, arrange housework for the nanny.

录音文本

Unit 1　你好！

一、　nín hěn rén

guó guì nǐ nǎ

二、　jiào wǒ yě guó shì yīng

三、　shì hěn běn guì nǐ

四、　1. 你好！　2. 您贵姓？　3. 我不是英国人。　4. 您是哪国人？

五、　1. 你好！

2. 您贵姓？

3. 我是中国人。

4. 你是哪国人？

5. 你是美国人吗？

Unit 2　现在几点？

一、　xiàn tiān diǎn bàn

hào huí hěn

二、　qù yuè qī jǐ huí

三、　jǐ hào xīng qù shì jiā

四、　1. ①七点一刻 ②七点零五分 ③差五分七点 ④七点四十五分

2. ①星期四，16号 ②星期一，13号 ③19号，星期日 ④18号，星期六

五、　1. 男：现在几点？

女：七点。

问：现在几点？

2. 男：你几号去北京？

女：我十二号去北京，二十号回上海。

问：几号回上海？

3. 男：今天八号，星期三。

问：十号星期几？

Unit 3　那件毛衣怎么卖?

一、　mài tài xiǎo máo

máo mǎi guǒ gōng

二、　pián duō liǎng zhè shén yǒu yào hóng yī xíng

三、　xíng mài dà tài cǎo

四、　1.一点儿　2.你买多少?　3.太小了，有大的吗?　4.我要红的。

五、　1.草莓要两斤。

2.这件夹克怎么卖?

3.我买苹果。

4.有红的吗?

六、　男：苹果怎么卖?

女：三块五一斤。

男：便宜点儿，行吗?

女：三块。要多少?

男：要四斤。

Unit 4　要一个宫保鸡丁

一、　cān dān kàn fàn

huā hú hē hái

二、　wǎn bié zhāng là jié zhàng

三、　zāi shàng gěi yàobiéde suānlàtāng

四、　1. ①一只烤鸭 ②一壶花茶 ③一双筷子 ④一碗米饭

2. ①打包 ②别放味精 ③结账 ④请给我一张餐巾纸

五、　1. 男：请给我一把勺子。

女：好。给您。

问：男的要什么?

2. 男：要一个宫保鸡丁。

女：还要别的吗?

男：再要一个酸辣汤。

问：男的要什么汤？

3. 女：您喝什么？

男：有什么？

女：有花茶、绿茶、啤酒、可乐。

男：要一壶绿茶。

问：男的要喝什么？

Unit 5 你在哪儿工作？

一、 zāi kǒu gōng shuí

jiě jīn jǐ jiā

二、 tā zuō yǒu dà suì

三、 mā shuài zuō xuě suì cōng

四、 1. 我爸爸在医院上班，他是医生。

2.3. 我姐姐很高，我妈妈很瘦。

五、 1. 男：你今年多大？

女：十二岁。

问：她现在多大？

2. 男：你在哪里工作？

女：我在医院工作，我是护士。

问：她做什么工作？

3. 男：我家有四口人，爸爸、妈妈、弟弟和我。

问：他家有几口人？

Unit 6 珍妮在吗？

一、 děng péng zhǎo shāo

wèi wēn dǎ diān

二、 jiū zhǎo cuō gěi huà qǐng tā shāo

三、 qǐng zhǎo cuō tā péng dǎ jiū diànhuà

四、 1. 您找谁？ 2. 他去饭店了。

3. 马丁不在。 4. 我是他的姐姐张华。

五、 1. 您找谁？ 2. 您哪位？ 3. 珍妮去哪儿了？

六、 男：喂！你好！你找谁？

女：你好！王先生在吗？

男：我就是。您哪位？

女：我叫李华，是你儿子的老师。

Unit 7 一直走

一、 zǒu dào gōng jī

lǜ guǎi zǒu

二、 shàng xíng kāi tiě yuǎn

三、 xué guǎi piào shī fēn yào

四、 A：学校怎么走？

B：一直走，第二个十字路口往左拐。

A：商店怎么走？

B：一直走，到红绿灯往右拐。

A：公司怎么走？

B：一直走，到丁字路口往东拐。

五、 1. 男：你每天怎么去上班？

女：骑自行车。

问：她每天怎么去上班？

2. 男：你家离公司远吗？

女：很远。

问：她家离公司近吗？

3. 男：骑自行车去要多长时间？

女：30 分钟。

问：骑自行车去要多长时间？

Unit 8 你的新家在哪儿？

一、 shàng páng fáng

xià xīn xiǎo

二、 yuán yàng chāo shì tīng

三、 bēi jī xì zhēn zē fú

四、 1. ①爸爸在妈妈左边 ②女儿在儿子后边

③妈妈在儿子左边 ④爸爸在女儿前边

2. ①盘子里边有一个苹果 ②盘子旁边有一个苹果

③盘子下面有一个苹果 ④盘子上边有一个苹果。

五、 1. 男：我的米饭呢？

女：在冰箱里面。

问：米饭在哪儿？

2. 男：听说你姐姐在学校工作。

女：是啊，她是老师。

问：姐姐在哪儿工作？

3. 男：公园附近有超市吗？

女：找过了，没有。

问：超市在公园附近吗？

Unit 9 你怎么了？

一、 mào gào bǎn gǎn

tóu téng shuō shuǐ

二、 yī xiū bìng shuǐ kē fā xǐ yào tóu gāo

三、 shuō mào bǎn xǐ shuǐ děi xǐhuan kēsou chīyào

四、 1. 头 2. 胳膊 3. 眼睛 4. 手 5. 脸 6. 肚子 7. 脚 8. 腿 9. 牙 10. 嘴

五、 1. 我感冒了。 2. 我有一点儿牙疼。

3. 你得找医生看看。 4. 我今天不能上课了。

六、 1. 你怎么了？ 2. 你头疼吗？ 3. 你喜欢喝酒吗？

七、 1. 女：马丁，你怎么了？
男：我有点儿不舒服。
女：你病了吗？
男：不，我累了。
2. 男：喂，丽丽，我是张华。我中午不能和你一起吃饭了。
女：为什么？
男：我有点儿头疼，得去药店买药。

Unit 10 你会修电脑吗？

一、 cháng fáng xiū qiú
huì hòu kōng kě

二、 yǐ dú nǎo zhōu cì mò qǐ jiàn shēn wǎng

三、 xiū kòng fáng nǎo huì huá hàn huāi

四、 1. 爬山 2. 滑冰 3. 开车 4. 健身 5. 骑车
6. 散步 7. 画画 8. 游泳 9. 做饭 10. 看书

五、 1. 下班以后我常常去游泳。
2. 周末我常常去买东西。
3. 晚饭以后我总是去公园散步。
4. 周末我有时候去爬山。

六、 （男）今天是星期一，下班以后我要去游泳。我很喜欢游泳，一星期要去三次。有时候我还去健身房健身。我也很喜欢打网球，会一点儿，打得不太好。

Unit 11 太冷了！

一、 zhuàng chuāng shuǎng suàn
rè ráo rěn

二、 chù wǎn zuì lǚ téng

三、 rì zé chú dǎo yīng sū

四、 1. ①零下47度 ②零度 ③29度 ④零下19度

2. ①晴，38度 ②下雨，12度 ③下雪，零下12度 ④刮风，8度

五、 1. 男：今天的气温是多少度？

女：零下三度。

问：今天的气温是多少度？

2. 男：纽约的气温是多少度？

女：零下二度。

男：旧金山的气温是多少度？

女：十三度。

问：纽约的天气怎么样？

3. 男：今天下雨了吗？

女：天气预报说今天有大雨，可是今天没下雨。

问：今天下雨了吗？

Unit 12 请把桌子擦一下儿？

一、 jiān qiǎn cā chā

shēn sháo xǐ xiā

二、 ā yí yùn sǎo huār wài xǐ lìng

三、 qiǎn chā wǎn fàn sháo bǎ shēng yíxiàr

四、 1. ①书房②厨房③客厅④卧室⑤卫生间

2. ①衣柜②床③沙发④书柜⑤茶几

3. ①勺子②杯子③盘子④筷子⑤花瓶

五、 1. 今天晚上我去饭店。 2. 那些衣服要洗吗？

3. 请把水果洗一下。 4. 把这些筷子放到桌子上。

六、 1. 请把这些水果洗一下。 2. 这些蔬菜要不要洗？

3. 今天你晚点儿走，行吗？ 4. 把鱼放到冰箱里吗？

课后练习参考答案

Unit 1 你好!

一、 n h r uo ui i a

二、 jiāo wǒ yě guó shì yīng

三、 shì hěn běn guì nǐ

四、 1.你好! 2.您贵姓? 3.我不是英国人。 4.您是哪国人?

五、 1.C 2.D 3.B 4.E 5.A

六、 nín hǎo hěn rén shì nǎ

七、 1.姓 2.是 3.很 4.哪 5.吗 6.呢 7.也 8.不

八、 1.他也是中国人。2.他是中国人吗? 3.他不是中国人。

九、 A:你是哪国人?

B:我是中国人。你呢?

A:我是美国人。您贵姓?

B:我姓张,叫张华。

十、 略。

十一、略。

十二、1.(1)姓张 (2)张彦 (3)200567 (4)85884433

2.(1)刘 (2)刘勇 (3)中国人 (4)188cm (5)74kg。

十三、也3 叫5 好6 我7 姓8 是9

十四、参考答案:1.你 他 2.好 姓 3.叫 哪 吗 呢

十五、略。

十六、略。

Unit 2 现在几点?

一、 x t d b ao ui en

二、 qù yuè qī jǐ huí

三、 jǐ hào xīng qù shì jiā

四、 1.②-①-④-③ 2.②-④-①-③

五、 1.B 2.B 3.B

六、 qù xiànzài jīntiān xīngqī

七、 1.你几点回家? 2.星期六是几号?

八、 1.前天、昨天、明天、后天 2.上午、下午、晚上

九、 1. 你几点上班？

2. 我星期三去北京。

3. 今天星期五，九月二十号。/今天九月二十号，星期五。

十、 略。

十一、略。

十二、1. （1）上午八点开始上课。晚上最后一节课到九点。

（2）每天十二节课。

（3）上午第三节十点十分上课，下午第三节三点半下课。

2. （1）王先生19号上午去上海，21号下午回北京。

（2）星期二上午见客户。

（3）星期四是22号。

（4）23号上午开会。

（5）24号/星期六晚上朋友聚会。

3. （1）这个学期一共有18个星期。

（2）2月20号开始上课，6月26号开始放假。

（3）运动会是4月21号到4月23号。

（4）“五一”放假九天。

（5）毕业典礼是7月3号、4号。

十三、几2 点9 回6 家10 月4 号5

十四、1. 日 2. 月 3. 曰

十五、略。

十六、略。

Unit 3 那件毛衣怎么卖？

一、 m t x m ao ai uo ong

二、 piān duō liǎng zhē shén yǒu yào hōng yī xíng

三、 xíng mǎi dǎ tǎi cǎo

四、 1. 一点儿 2. 你买多少？ 3. 太小了，有大的吗？ 4. 我要红的。

五、 1. 两 2. 这 3. 苹果 4. 红

六、 1.B 2.A 3.C

七、 1. 件 2. 条 3. 套 4. 斤/个 5. 双

八、 大—小，瘦—胖，贵—便宜，厚—薄，这—那，买—卖，长—短。

九、 1. 一共多少钱？ 2. 这双皮鞋怎么卖？ 3. 有小的吗？

十、 1. 这条裤子怎么卖？/那条裤子怎么卖？/裤子多少钱一条？

2. 有黑的吗？

3. 我试试，行吗？

4. 太短了，有长的吗？

5. 太贵了，便宜一点儿，行吗？

十一、1. (1)1800元 (2)2006年4月9日

2. (1)草莓和苹果 (2)39.7元 (3)2006年7月19日

十二、3画：么

4画：什 少 斤

6画：买 多

7画：两 块

10画：钱

十三、艹 钅 土 彳 亻 讠 纟 辶

十四、略。

十五、略。

Unit 4 要一个宫保鸡丁

一、 c d k f ua u e ai

二、 wǎn bié zhāng là jié zhàng

三、 zāi shàng gěi yào bié de suānlàtāng

四、 1. ④-②-③-① 2. ②-③-④-①

五、 1.B. 一把勺子 2.B. 酸辣汤 3.B. 绿茶

六、 chá wǎn cài mǐfàn jīdīng jiézhàng

七、 1.要一个宫保鸡丁。 2.请给我一张餐巾纸。 3.结账。

八、 1.张 个 斤 壶 双

2.没 还 别 再 能

九、 1.请给我一张餐巾纸。

2.我们的烤鸭还没上。

十、 1.A 2.B 3.B。

十一、略。

十二、1. ④这是菜单，请点菜。

①我要一只烤鸭，再要一个麻婆豆腐。

③您喝什么？

②有什么？

⑤有可乐、啤酒，还有花茶。

⑥我要一听可乐。

2. 略。

3. (1) 答案：川菜，鲁菜，淮扬菜，粤菜；肯德基，麦当劳，好伦哥，必胜客

(2) 略。

十三、请10 菜11 喝12 账8 鸡7 汤6 茶9 纸7

十四、略。

十五、略。

Unit 5 你在哪儿工作？

一、 z k g sh ie in i ia

二、 tā zuō yǒu dā suì

三、 mā shuāi zuō xuē suì cōng

四、 1.B 2.D 3.A

五、 1.A 2.A 3.B

六、 tā hé shuí gōngzuō lǎoshī

七、 1.我家有四口人。2.他们是谁？ 3.你家有什么人？

八、 (一) 1. 丈夫 妻子

2.Sam Sophie 丈夫 父亲

3. 女儿 Lily 姐姐

4. 儿子 弟弟 哥哥

5.Peter Laura 妹妹

(二) 1.Sam 家有七口人。

2.(参考答案) Peter 在医院工作。

3.(参考答案) Laura 是老师。

4.Sam 73 岁，Sophie 69 岁。

5.Peter 今年 40 岁，Laura 39 岁，Lucy 17 岁，Paul13 岁。

6.Lily 今年 6 岁。

九、 1.你在哪儿工作？ 2.我家有四口人。 3.我哥哥三十岁。

十、 略。

十一、略。

十二、口3 年6 岁6 哥10 作7 高10

十三、1. 亻 2. 女

十四、答案举例：1. 你爸爸在哪儿工作？ 2. 你家有什么人？

3. 那人是谁？ 4. 今年你多大？

5. 你弟弟几岁了？ 6. 你爷爷多大年纪了？

7. 你家有几口人？　　　　8. 你有几个姐姐？

十五、医生 . 护士 . 会计 . 律师 . 秘书 . 保安 . 服务员 . 公司职员 . 大使 . 司机

十六、略。

Unit 6 珍妮在吗？

一、　d p zh sh　ei en a ian

二、　jiū zhǎo cuō gěi huā qǐng tā shāo

三、　qǐng zhǎo cuō tā péng dǎ jiù diànhuà

四、　1. 您找谁？　　　　2. 他去饭店了。

　　　3. 马丁不在。　　　4. 我是他的姐姐张华。

五、　1. A　2. B　3. B

六、　1. 误 2. 正 3. 正 4. 正 5. 误

七、　参考答案：1. 他，她 2. 喂，位 3. 电，店 4. 是，试

八、　1. 找 2. 在 3. 就 4. 位 5. 错 6. 给

九、　1. 马丁在不在？ 2. 我就是马丁。 3. 他去银行了。 4. 我是他的朋友。

十、　略。

十一、A：喂！你好！

　　　B：喂！你好！/ 你找谁？

　　　A：张华在吗？/ 在不在？

　　　B：我就是。/ 在，请稍等。/ 你打错了。

十二、1. 这是妈妈给丽丽留的便条。

　　　2. 马丁给丽丽打电话了。下午三点半打的。

　　　3. 丽丽下午去银行了。

　　　4. 马丁请丽丽给他回电话。

　　　5. 马丁的电话是65323665。

　　　6. 参考答案：

珍妮：

你的朋友张华给你打电话，你去商店了。张华请你给她回电话，

她的电话是13601237445。

阿 姨

x月x日

十三、友4　打5　问6　找7　朋8　给9　喂12　错13

十四、①问 ②朋 ③找 ④位 ⑤作 ⑥什 ⑦做

十五、略。

十六、略。

Unit 7 一直走

一、 z d g j ü uai ou

二、 shàng xíng kāi tiě yuǎn

三、 xué guǎi piào shī fēn yào

四、

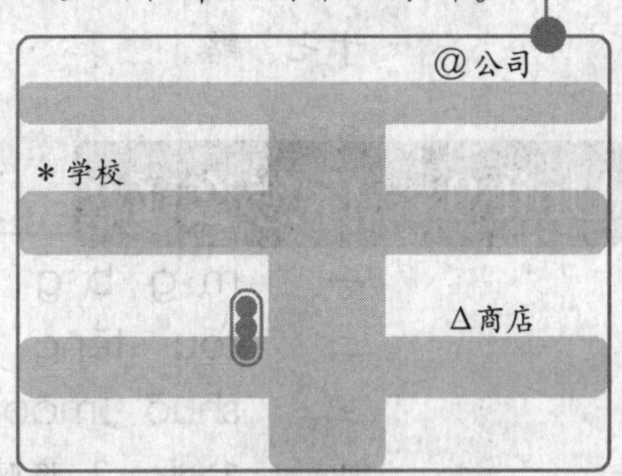

五、 1.B 2.A 3.B

六、 guǎi hónglǜdēng fāpiào dǔchē

七、 1.你知道去那儿怎么走吗？ 2.为什么不开车？

八、 1.你去哪儿？ 2.去你家怎么走？ 3.坐出租车去要十五分钟。

九、 略。

十、 略。

十一、略。

十二、车4 直8 停11 分4 堵11 着11

十三、1.辶 2.彳 3.亻

十四、略。

十五、略。

Unit 8 你的新家在哪儿？

一、 sh p f iā īn iǎo

二、 yuán yàng chāo shì tīng

三、 bēi jī xì zhēn zě fú

四、 1.③-①-②-④ 2.④-③-①-②

五、 1.B 2.A 3.B

六、 fūrén zázhì yuánlái bānjiā

七、 1.我的新家在飞机场附近。2.书柜里有一本红色的中文书。

八、 1.上边，下边，左边，右边 2.外边，里边，旁边，中间

九、 1.马路对面有一辆自行车。 2.你妹妹的新工作怎么样？

3.医院在超市附近。/超市在医院附近。

十、 略。

十一、我搬家了。我的爸爸妈妈都在美国大使馆工作，我们的新家在大使馆

附近，在一栋很大的公寓里。公寓很漂亮，也很方便，马路对面是银行和医院。医院旁边有一个中国饭馆。我很喜欢这个饭馆的菜。

十二、1. 略。

2. (1)美国在南边，加拿大在北边。

(2)中国在西边，日本在东边。

(3)英国在西北边，法国在中间，德国在东北边，西班牙在西南边。

十三、1. “勺园”在学校的西边。

2. 工商银行附近有邮局和商店。

3. 先往东，再往南一直走。

4. “农园”的东边有“三教”、“四教”和“五四篮球场”。

5. 参考答案：应该建在学校南边，因为离宿舍区比较近。

十四、对5　旁10　边5　本5　里7　亮9

十五、1. 木　2. 饣　3. ⺮

十六、略。

十七、略。

Unit 9　你怎么了？

一、　m g b g　ou eng uo ui

二、　tóu téng shuō shuǐ

三、　shuō mào bǎn xǐ shuǐ děi xǐhuan kēsou chīyào

四、　1. 头　2. 胳膊　3. 眼睛　4. 手　5. 脸　6. 肚子　7. 脚　8. 腿　9. 牙　10. 嘴

五、　1. 我感冒了。　2. 我有一点儿牙疼。

3. 你得找医生看看。　4. 我今天不能上课了。

六、　1.A　2.A　3.B

七、　1.A　2.A

八、　1. 烧　稍　2. 一　医　3. 要　药

九、　1. 喝　2. 吃　3. 吃　4. 喝　5. 喝　6. 喝

十、　1. 看　2. 吃　3. 有点儿　4. 一点儿

十一、1. 我有一点儿不舒服。2. 你得去医院看病。　3. 我不能去上课了。

十二、1. 宋丽丽不能去上课。她感冒了，有点儿头疼。

2. 她的老师姓张。　3. 她请一天假。

十三、1. 亻　2. 心　3. 疒　4. 木

十四、①休　②息　③感　④本　⑤柜　⑥疼　⑦病

十五、略。

十六、略。

Unit 10 你会修电脑吗？

一、 ch f x q　ui ou ong e

二、 yǐ dú nǎo zhōu cì mò qǐ jiàn shēn wǎng

三、 xiū kōng fáng nǎo huì huá hàn huài

四、 1.爬山　2.滑冰　3.开车　4.健身　5.骑车
6.散步　7.画画　8.游泳　9.做饭　10.看书

五、 1.常常　2.周末　3.晚饭　4.有时候

六、 1.正　2.误　3.误　4.正　5.误

七、 xiū diànnǎo kěnéng zhōumò xiàbān huì

八、 参考答案：1.电脑、电话　3.上网、上班
2.生病、病毒　4.书房、健身房

九、 1.他会不会说汉语？　2.他会说汉语吗？　3.他不会说汉语。

十、 1.我会一点儿。　2.我们一起去健身房吧。
3.听说你会修车。　4.他打得很好。

十一、略。

十二、1.游泳　三　打网球　散步　在家休息　买东西　看书　看电视
2.略。

十三、会6　网6　坏7　空8　毒9　修9　脑10　常11　球11

十四、参考答案：1.打 找　2.朋 脑　3.行 得

十五、略。

十六、略。

Unit 11 太冷了！

一、 zh ch sh s　e ao en

二、 chū wǎn zuì lǔ téng

三、 rì zé chū dǎo yīng sū

四、 1.①-④-③-②　2.③-①-④-②

五、 1.A　2.B　3.B

六、 nuǎnhuo xiàxuě lǚxíng língxià

七、 1.那儿的气温是多少度？　2.天气预报说今天有大雨。

八、 1. 北京:零下十度（零下的温度都可以）　香港:三十度（比较高的温度都可以）
2. 7号:十五度左右都可以　10号:零下二度

九、 1.冬天比春天冷多了。　2.天气预报说今天会下雨。

3. 昨天早上我没去游泳。

十、 参考答案：很漂亮 很冷 零下10度 低很多 要下雨 没带 借了

十一、1. (1) 昨天的天气预报说今天没有雨。
(2) 马丁没淋雨。
(3) 马丁原计划今天去爬山。
2. (1) 王先生计划星期三去公园散步，不能去。
(2) 王先生计划星期五去游泳，能去。
(3) 这个星期星期一天气最好。
(4) 这个星期星期天天气最差。这一天王先生计划去健身房健身。这个星期星期六天气最差，这一天王先生计划去爬山。
(5) 这个星期王先生能做五项运动。

十二、气4 温12 冷7 雨8 晴12 零13

十三、略。

十四、略。

Unit 12 请把桌子擦一下儿？

一、 j q c ch en ao i ia

二、 ā yí yūn sǎo huār wài xǐ lìng

三、 qiǎn chā wǎn fàn shāo bǎ shēng yíxiàr

四、 1. ⑤-②-④-①-③ 2. ⑤-③-①-④-② 3. ④-①-⑤-②-③

五、 1. 今天晚上我去饭店。 2. 那些衣服要洗吗？
3. 请把水果洗一下。 4. 把这些筷子放到桌子上。

六、 1.A 2.B 3.A 4.A

七、 shēn qiǎn xǐ dǎsǎo shuǐguǒ wǎn shūcài fàn

八、 参考答案：1. 书、蔬；2. 快、筷；3. 碗、晚。

九、 1. 沙发 2. 书 3. 把 4. 厨房

十、 1. 熨 2. 擦 3. 插 4. 放

十一、1. 那碗放到厨房里。 2. 把书放到桌子上。
3. 把毛衣放到衣柜里。 4. 把草莓放到碗里。

十二、1. 请朋友到家里吃饭。 2. 去商店买东西了。
3. 收拾厨房 洗衣服 打扫卫生间 把窗台上的花放到桌子上

十三、 衣6 把7 浅8 洗9 瓶10 深11 碗13 擦17

十四、 ①把 ②擦 ③冷 ④洗 ⑤瓶 ⑥碗 ⑦爸

十五、略。

十六、略。

图书在版编目（CIP）数据

体验汉语（生活篇）练习册 / 宋海燕，詹成峰编. —北京：高等教育出版社，2006.10（2009 重印）

ISBN 978 - 7 - 04 - 020491 - 9

Ⅰ. 体... Ⅱ. ①宋... ②詹... Ⅲ. 汉语 - 对外汉语教学 - 习题 Ⅳ. H195.4 - 44

中国版本图书馆 CIP 数据核字（2006）第 121713 号

出版发行	高等教育出版社	购书热线	010 - 58581118
社　　址	北京市西城区德外大街 4 号	免费咨询	800 - 810 - 0598
邮政编码	100120	网　　址	http://www.hep.edu.cn
总　　机	010 - 58581000		http://www.hep.com.cn
		网上订购	http://www.landraco.com
			http://www.landraco.com.cn
经　　销	蓝色畅想图书发行有限公司	畅想教育	http://www.widedu.com
印　　刷	高等教育出版社印刷厂		
开　　本	889 × 1194　1/16		
印　　张	8.75	版　　次	2006 年 10 月第 1 版
字　　数	250 000	印　　次	2009 年 8 月第 4 次印刷

本书如有印装等质量问题，请到所购图书销售部门调换。

ISBN 978 - 7 - 04 - 020491 - 9

02800

物料号　20491 - 00